MONEY
TO CARE

MONEY TO CARE

Hospital Finance
For Non-Financial Hospital Leaders

Denise Harrison Chamberlain

Money to Care
Hospital Finance For Non-Financial Hospital Leaders

© 2010, Money to Care, LLC. All rights reserved.

ISBN: 978-0-615-42299-2

LCCN: 2010941602

Design: OPA Author Services, Scottsdale, AZ & Krause Creative, Phoenix, AZ
Printed by Snowfall Press, Monument, CO and Phoenix, AZ

Published by Money to Care, LLC.
All correspondence to the publisher should be addressed to
29523 North 146th Street, Scottsdale, Arizona 85262

Printed in the United States of America

Dedication

To Aiden and Ella —
May this book bring me closer quicker,
and
To My Dad—Simply The Best

Table of Contents

Foreword

Did you just get a promotion? Maybe you've been a manager for many years. But if you're reading this book, I'm assuming you are in healthcare but do not have a financial background. So it is probably safe to assume that the financial responsibilities of your job are perhaps the least fun thing you do. You didn't get into healthcare to crunch numbers and count money, after all. You got into it to take care of people, to do "feel-good" things every day. And finance isn't a "feel-good" thing for you, is it? But maybe it can be.

I'm not proposing that this book will make you want to return to school and get an accounting degree. But what I do hope is that it will make handling the finance part of your job a little easier, a little less stressful, and maybe it will get you through it quicker so you can get back to doing the things that bring you more joy and satisfaction.

I've been in healthcare finance for 25 years. Almost exclusively in hospitals. So this is my reference point. But this book is not meant to be a reference guide for finance professionals. The definitions are my words, based on my experiences. I do not cover mergers and acquisitions or Wall Street financing. The topics I have chosen to cover are the ones I have found over the years that healthcare managers struggle with the most—the ones you need to deal with every day.

I am a person who cannot remember anything that I don't understand, so my hope for this book is that it will help you *understand* the pieces of the healthcare finance puzzle of that affect you. My goal is to present the material in the way I think and hope a non-financial manager can best grasp it. So let's get started!

Introduction

There are many ways to measure success. Money is only one of them. And it is important to understand that financial results are just (and only) a measure of success. They are a means to an end; they are not the goal.

Financial results are the outcome. They are historic. Even one split second after they happen—it is still after the fact. Financial results tell the story after it happens. It's like reading a diary.

Many people say finance is a "foreign language" to them, that they do not understand it at all. "It's all Greek to me," they say. And in a way, it is. Financial reporting is a "language" used to tell the story of what happened. If you speak the language, you can look at the financial statements and understand what they are telling you, and the story is told. If you don't speak the language, then you won't be able to read the story. It won't matter if it's in English, Spanish or French. You hear attorneys talk about legal-ese. I am hoping this book will help you better understand *finance-ese*.

Financial statements do nothing more than tell a story. That is true no matter who is looking at them. It can be a Wall Street financier working on a stock offering, a local banker looking to loan money to a start-up business, or you looking at your departmental financials. If you know finance-ese, you can look at any financials and know the story. Finance-ese is a language with a large vocabulary. We will focus on the words and meanings that *you* need to know to understand, review, and discuss *your* financials. You don't have to understand the whole language to do that any more than you need to know the entire French language to order a cup of coffee in Paris.

I can't tell you how many times I have watched people roll their eyes when finance comes up during a discussion. "It's all about the money with you people." Well, yes, the money is our job. But that doesn't mean we think nothing else is important. Think about it for a moment. Why is money important to you? Because you want to have a whole bunch of it in your pocket to look at? I doubt it. Money is only important for what it can do. For you. To be able to own a home. Take your family on vacation. Send your child to college. Support causes near to your heart.

It's the same with your company.

Section I

Hospital Finance Overview

Hospital Terms: Definitions, Acronyms And Ratios

Note: Rather than simply to provide an alphabetical listing of terms, the sequence of terms used here is arranged so you'll be able to build on your knowledge from one term to the next.

Patient Day: When one patient spends one day *as an inpatient* at the hospital, it equals one patient day. Over the course of a month, the Patient Days for the month is the total of all such days. If exactly 100 patients are in the hospital each day, at the end of a 30-day month, the hospital will have had 3,000 (30 x 100) Patient Days.

Inpatient vs. Observation: When a physician determines that a patient needs hospital care, he/she may write orders to admit the patient either as an Inpatient or an Observation patient. For caregivers, the difference is meaningless. Their responsibilities are the same: care for the patient. The financial difference, though, is how the hospital is paid for the care. See **Chapter 2** for further discussion on the differences.

Census: The number of patients in-house at a point in time. The definition technically refers to inpatients, but many times, the response also includes patients in beds for observation. For example, if there are 42 patients in beds as inpatients, and eight patients currently in beds for Observation, if a person is asked "what's census?" the response may be either "42" or "50"— which is why you frequently then hear the person who asked the original question add, "Does that include Observation?"

Midnight Census: Census fluctuates throughout any given day as patients are admitted and discharged. The midnight census is usually the one a hospital will record and keep for historical tracking purposes. It is an industry standard that allows hospitals to compare themselves against each other, and more importantly—from a finance perspective—it is the census a hospital is paid on. If a patient is admitted at 12:01 a.m. on Monday, and discharged at 11:59 p.m. on Tuesday, although the patient was under the hospital's care for 47 hours and 58 minutes, for reimbursement purposes, the patient was only in-house for one midnight census (at midnight Monday evening). This may mean the hospital's reimbursement is based on *one* day. Likewise, if that same patient was instead admitted at 11:59 p.m. Sunday and discharged at 12:01 a.m. Tuesday, although the patient was under hospital care for 48 hours and 2 minutes, the hospital may be reimbursed for three days, because the patient was in-house at midnight Sunday, Monday and Tuesday. See Chapter 2 for further discussion.

Average Daily Census (ADC): ADC is the average of the daily census over a period of time—usually a month or a year, although any period may be used. Comparing the monthly or annual ADC over times indicates if hospital volumes are increasing or decreasing. The calculation is simply the sum of midnight censuses over the period, divided by the number of days in the period. For example: the ADC for a week where the midnight census each evening was: 203, 158, 195, 172, 187, 199, and 173 is computed as (203+158+195+172+187+199+173)/7 = 184.

Adjusted Patient Days (APDs): APDs is a term that was created to permit valid comparisons over time between hospitals—or across all departments in one hospital. Although not a perfect measurement, it is useful for many financial and operational measurements and comparisons. While most hospital Nursing units provide care predominantly to inpatients, some departments may provide services to a mixture of inpatients and outpatients; Surgery, Imaging and Laboratory are three of the most common examples. In order to calculate measurements such as revenue and labor productivity, it was necessary to devise a common measure that encompassed both inpatient and the outpatient business. The APD does just that. The theory is that in terms of value and/or resource utilization, $1 of inpatient revenue is equal in value and/or resource utilization to $1 of outpatient revenue. Example: if the average *inpatient day* in a given month generates, say, $10,000, then each $10,000 of outpatient revenue generated during the same period must be equivalent to one *inpatient day*. To further illustrate, if a hospital generated $1,000,000 of inpatient revenue on a given day while taking care of 100 inpatients, then on average, each inpatient generated $10,000 ($1,000,000/100). If the same hospital, on that same day, generated $500,000 of outpatient revenue, then outpatient revenue (for APD purposes) generated the equivalent of 50 additional patient days ($500,000/$10,000). Said in another way, Adjusted Patient Days reflects the sum of inpatient days and equivalent outpatient days. In our example, the APDs for the hospital that day were 100 inpatient days + 50 equivalent days, for a total of 150 APDs.

Adjustment Factor: The adjustment factor is a shortcut to computing APDs, or Adjusted Discharges, or Adjusted Census. To compute the Adjustment factor, apply a simple formula:

$$\frac{\textbf{Total Inpatient + Outpatient revenue for the period}}{\textbf{Total Inpatient revenue for the period}}$$

The resulting adjustment factor will always be a number greater than 1. That number may then be multiplied by any inpatient statistic to arrive at an "adjusted statistic"—for example:

- inpatient days x adjustment factor = APDs

- inpatient discharges x adjustment factor = adjusted discharges.

An arithmetic example: If the patient days over a month period were 3,000, and the adjustment factor is 1.5, the APDs would be 3,000 x 1.5 = 4,500. This implies that although the inpatient business was 3,000 patient days, the hospital provided services equal to what would have been required if there had been 4,500 patient days.

Adjusted Occupied Beds (AOB): Adjusted Occupied Beds is an indicator of census that applies the adjustment factor. For example, if the census (or ADC) is 100, and the Adjustment factor is 1.8, then the AOB is 180 (100 x 1.8). This means that even though the inpatient census is 100, the hospital needs resources to care for an equivalent of 180 patients because so many outpatient services are being rendered that it is as if there are 180 patients in the hospital rather than just 100. This statistic becomes useful when measuring labor productivity and efficiency across all departments in the hospital.

Gross Charges: A patient is charged for all services he receives while at the hospital. The sum of all of the charges for all patients is called Gross Charges. Gross charges is rarely the amount that the hospital gets paid.

Net Revenue or Net Collectible Revenue: Net Revenue refers to the amount that a hospital expects to get paid, based on contractual agreements with payors and agreements with uninsured patients. Net collectible revenue is Net Revenue less the amount the hospital ends up writing off to bad debt. See Chapter 2 for further discussion.

Contractual Allowances and Other Revenue Deductions: Contractual Allowances are the difference between gross charges and the amount that the hospital contractually agreed to accept as reimbursement for care. Contractual allowances are a revenue deduction. Other revenue deductions include charity write offs and self pay discounts. Bad Debt is NOT a revenue deduction. It is an operating expense. See **Chapter 2** for further discussion.

Case Mix Index ("CMI"): The weighted average sum of all of a hospital's DRG weights over a period of time is called the Case Mix Index ("CMI"). For example, if a hospital took care of three patients; one patient had a diagnosis with a case weight of .56, and the other two had diagnoses with a case weight of 1.28, then the hospital's CMI would be (.56 + 1.28 + 1.28)/3 = 1.04. See Chapter 2 for further discussion.

Financial Class and Payor Mix: Hospitals group patients into like groups based on how they are paid. Ten patients may have 10 different managed care plans, but will all be grouped together under a financial class called Managed Care. Each hospital has their own groupings, but the most common are Medicare, Managed Care, Medicaid, and Self Pay. What percentage of a hospital's patients fall into each financial class is called payor mix. Payor mix must add up to 100%. An example payor mix might be 55% Medicare, 25% Managed Care, 15% Medicaid, and 5% Self Pay. See Chapter 2 for further discussion.

Man Hours: Man Hours are the sum of all hours either paid or worked during a specific period of time. For example, if a department had two employees and one worked 40 hours and took no time off, while the other employee worked 20 hours and took 20 paid hours off on sick leave, then paid Man Hours would be 80 (40+40), while worked Man Hours would be 60 (40+20).

Paid or Worked, Productive or Non-Productive: Employees are paid to work. But they are usually also paid while on vacation, bereavement, jury duty, attending an educational seminar, etc. The hours that an employee spends doing his hired task are called worked hours. They are also called productive hours. Time spent doing other things is called Non-Productive hours. Paid hours is the sum of Productive and Non-Productive hours.

Full Time Equivalent (FTE): An FTE is a term used to measure labor resources in a common way. Hospitals employ many part-time staff, and many facilities consider "fulltime" to be less than 40 hours a week. FTE is used to measure labor: By definition, one FTE works the number of hours an exempt full time employee would work during the period. A fulltime, exempt employee works 40 hours per week, or 2,080 hours per year. Full Time Equivalents are computed by dividing total hours over a specific time by the number of hours one FTE would work. So if the total of hours worked in a small department over a one week period was 200, then the department would have *five* FTEs, since 1 FTE works 40 hour a week. Seven or eight different employees may have actually done the work in many different combinations of hours, but the 200 total hours worked still represents *five* FTEs.

Department Statistic: Each department has a unit statistic relevant to its business. The department statistic is associated with the "task" that the department completes each day. A Nursing unit has patient days; Labs have lab tests; Radiology has x-rays; Dietary has meals; Medical Records has charts, and so on. For most departments, the actual statistic number is the volume of tasks that were done during the period (i.e., if the statistic for lab was 1,000 for the month, 1,000 lab tests were performed). Department volume is a key indicator for measuring the revenue and expenses of your department within your hospital's budget, and it may also be used to compare entire hospitals with other similar facilities.

Per Stat: Whether budgeting, reviewing month end results against budget, or comparing yourself to your peers at other hospitals, the best way to do things is on a "per statistic" (or "per stat") basis. As discussed above, each department in a hospital has it's own statistic, so when you look at things on a "per stat" basis, it automatically adjusts for variances in departmental volume and department size. On various financial documents and in spreadsheets, you may see all kinds of things referred to on a "per stat" basis—revenue per stat (rev/stat), salaries/stat, supplies/stat, man hours/stat, etc. This way of expressing things makes comparisons more useful. For example, if you are a lab director, and you want to look at data from your peers to see how you compare in operating efficiencies, it is not useful to simply compare your number of FTEs to theirs. You may have less, but that doesn't necessarily mean you are more efficient. You may, in fact, be less efficient if you perform significantly fewer tests. If you have fewer FTEs per test (the standard stat for lab), then yes, you can feel good that you are more efficient. Make sense?

Labor Productivity: Labor productivity is a measure of efficiency. It is an indicator of how many Man Hours will be (or were) utilized to complete a "task." As noted above, the "task" is the statistic relevant to the department being measured. For a Nursing unit, the task or statistic is a patient day. For pharmacy, it will be the issuance of a dose or prescription. For admitting, it will be completing one registration. The generic term to refer to productivity is "ManHours per Stat" or "MH/Stat."

Labor Management: Labor management is a term that is sometimes used interchangeably with the term Labor Productivity. Actually, Labor Productivity is just one part of Labor Management. Labor Management is the term to encompass *all* the things that impact labor costs. These include (besides productivity), managing contract labor, overtime, callback time, skill mix, and rates of pay.

Monthly Operating Review (MOR): An MOR is both a report and an event. The report is a document that summarizes a department, or an entire hospital's performance. It is more than a financial document. It usually includes a combination of quality, satisfaction and financial indicators. The event is a meeting to discuss the report.

Chapter 1 Self Review Questions

1. If your hospital's midnight census over the past week was 528, 578, 543, 509, 551, 537, and 549, what was the ADC for the week?

2. If your hospital had inpatient revenues of $1,597,231 and outpatient revenues of $782,344, what is your adjustment factor?

3. If your hospital had inpatient days totaling 10,168 during the month, and an adjustment factor of 1.83, how many APDs did you have?

4. If total worked hours during the most recent 14-day pay period in your department were 4,480, how many worked FTEs were there?

5. Your Lab Department's productivity is .15 MH/Stat. The lab in a competing hospital has a productivity stat of .20 MH/Stat. Who is more productive?

CDM and Reimbursement

Hospital reimbursement is very complicated and highly regulated. In this book, the discussion will be limited to the information you need to know to manage your department(s). The discussion will be very high-level.

Let's start with the "big picture." Hospitals generate two kinds of revenue: Patient Care Revenue is the accumulation of charges made to a patient during their stay; "Other Revenue" (or "Non-Patient Revenue") captures all other incomes. Cafeteria and gift shop sales are the most common types of Other Revenue.

We will focus here only on Patient Care Revenue.

CHARGE DESCRIPTION MASTER (CDM)

Just like other businesses, hospitals charge for their services. A patient is charged a daily room rate while an inpatient. Typically, charges are captured at midnight on each and every day, and charges may vary, depending on the level of care a given patient receives. The daily room charge covers room, meals, some routine supplies, and nursing care. All other services typically carry individual charges. If a patient has surgery, there will be surgery and anesthesia charges, as well as charges for lab tests, pharmacy, etc.

If you've ever ordered something from a catalogue, you can easily imagine a hospital "catalogue." It would include every service possibly offered, and each service or item would carry a price. All types of x-ray or MRI scan would be listed. Every drug. Every supply item. That *"catalogue"* is called a Charge Description Master—a CDM.

As a manager, you may be responsible for keeping your section of the CDM current. There is probably a form you complete and submit for approval if you want to add a new item or change the price of an item. The CDM interfaces with the billing system, and it captures and accumulates charges while a patient is receiving services at the hospital. These are referred to as **Gross Charges.** Most of the time, however, they have little to do with how much a hospital is actually paid.

Unlike most other industries, the consumer of hospital services (the patient) is not the payor in most cases.

Most patients are enrolled in some type of health plan. Working Americans are most often enrolled in a healthcare plan selected by their employer; senior citizens have Medicare; there are multiple government programs for the poor (such as Medicaid); and some of the poorest patients may qualify for charity. And some patients who do not have insurance but do not qualify for a government program or charity may simply not have the ability to pay their bills (or have the funds but choose not to), and the hospital must write their bill off as a bad debt after collection efforts fail.

The only patients who may pay for their own healthcare directly are those who cannot afford insurance, patients who are wealthy and choose not to carry health insurance, or foreigners who do not have access to US health plans.

REIMBURSEMENT

Inpatient and Outpatient Reimbursement (DRGs and Fee Schedules)

DRG stands for "Diagnosis Related Group." It is a term that Medicare and many other insurance companies use. Traditional Medicare pays the hospital a fixed amount for an *inpatient* stay, irrespective of how long the patient stays or what costs (or charges) were accumulated. The amount of the payment is tied to the diagnosis of the patient.

Medicare has its own list of diagnosis codes, called MS-DRGs. These codes are updated annually in response to changes in medicine. Each code is assigned a weight that indicates the relative severity of the diagnosis as compared to other diagnoses. A DRG with a weight of 1.50 is considered to be 1.5 times more severe (thus costlier to provide care for) than a DRG with a weight of 1.00. The higher the weight, the greater the payment to the hospital; that is, a DRG with a weight of 1.50 pays 150% of a DRG with a case weight of 1.00. For example, if a hospital payment for a DRG with a case weight of 1.00 was $8,000, then the payment for a DRG with a case weight of 1.50 would be $8,000 x 1.50 = $12,000.

The weighted average sum of all of a hospital's DRG weights over a period of time is called the Case Mix Index ("CMI"). For example, if a hospital took care of three patients; one patient had a diagnosis with a case weight of .56, and the other two had diagnoses with a case weight of 1.28, then the hospital's CMI would be (.56 + 1.28 + 1.28)/3 = 1.04.

The DRG is assigned before billing by a "Coder" based on the documentation found in the patient's chart. Many times, the only difference between whether a chart is coded (and therefore paid) as one DRG and not another is the physicians' documentation in the medical record. Many diagnoses have multiple DRG codes, depending on other procedures performed and other health issues present, including complications. The more complex the patient's issues, the higher the weight and the greater the payment—but only when the specific, case-related complexities are *documented* in the medical record by the patient's physician(s). You can see now why hospitals focus so much on working with physicians to document complete details in the patient's chart! If a patient is very sick, with numerous complications that result in the hospital spending more to care for the patient, and if the documentation of those complexities is not on the chart, the hospital will only be reimbursed for the lower level of care.

Even for the same DRG, a payment from Medicare may vary from one hospital to another. Because labor is approximately 50% of a hospital's operating cost, Medicare payments are adjusted for geographic differences in wages. Payments to hospitals in New York City, for example, are higher than in most other American cities because wages in NYC are significantly higher than in other U.S. metropolitan areas.

Not all payors pay based on DRGs. But many have adopted it. Since DRG reimbursement is fixed, hospitals can improve their financial results when they efficiently manage the costs associated with a patient's stay. Since labor is about half of a hospital's total expenses, managing labor means managing the number of days a patient stays. For example, if patients A and B both have the same DRG, then the hospital will be paid the same amount for both patients. Let's use a DRG payment of $10,000. If the hospital's costs are $2,000 per day and patient A stays three days while patient B stays six days, then the hospital makes $4,000 profit on patient A ($10,000—($2,000 x 3)), and loses $2,000 on patient B ($10,000—($2,000 x 6)).

Outpatient services are usually paid in a similar fashion; payment is based on a fee schedule (a price list) of all possible outpatient procedures that can be performed. These include lab work, diagnostics (MRI, radiology, CT, etc.), ER, outpatient surgery, and observation.

Observation

Patients in observation are considered to be outpatients and the hospital is paid according to its outpatient fee schedule. You probably know someone who went to the ER and was put into the hospital "for observation." This usually means that the examining physician doesn't think the patient needs to be admitted to the hospital but feels uncomfortable sending the patient home. He wants to "observe" for a while. If test results come back indicating an actual condition requiring hospitalization, the patient will then be admitted; if not, the physician will send the patient home—usually within 24 hours.

Observation was developed to bridge the gap between the physician and the insurance company. It allows the physician to keep an eye on a patient for a while, but if no admission follows, the insurance company is not "gouged" for a large payment.

From an insurance perspective, if a patient is admitted and ends up staying several days, the hospital will be paid the full DRG payment. But if the physician "admits" that person as an inpatient while observing—and no admittable condition is discovered and the patient is home 12 hours later, the insurance company will not pay the hospital a full DRG payment (remember, a full DRG payment may cover several days of care).

Medicare

Virtually all hospitals are Medicare providers, which means that they have agreed to Medicare's rules and regulations—and have agreed to accept Medicare reimbursement schedules.

Medicare is a federal program. "Part A" covers inpatient hospital services, while "Part B" covers outpatient services, doctor visits, etc. "Part D" is the pharmacy coverage that was added a few years ago. Most patients who qualify for Medicare are seniors (over 65), although Medicare also covers some other patients. Patients may enroll in "traditional" Medicare ("traditional" Medicare is the government-sponsored plan that for many years was the only option available), or they may have elected a Medicare Managed Care plan, which operates through a private-sector health insurance company. When a patient enrolls in a Medicare Managed Care plan, the Plan receives the money the government would have paid to care for the patient, and the Plan assumes the risk of whether or not that payment is enough to cover the amount billed by the hospital.

From the patient's perspective, both methods appear quite similar, but covered benefits may sometimes be different in a managed care plan than in the traditional Medicare plan.

From the hospital's perspective, however, a Medicare Managed Care plan is not fundamentally different from a managed care plan. In both cases, the hospital negotiates with the plan for payment rates, and most payment rates are closely tied to whatever Medicare would have paid the hospital.

Medicare often pays some hospitals extra money for things such as medical education programs and Medicare bad debts, but a discussion of such added reimbursements is beyond the scope of this book.

Medicaid

Medicaid is a program for the poor, administered by the states and generally covers citizens who are residents of that state. Who is covered, how reimbursement is structured, and how much a hospital is paid vary by state. Most state programs pay either a fixed amount per day or a fixed amount per discharge (similar to Medicare) for inpatient services, and these programs pay from a fee schedule for outpatient services (also similar to Medicare).

Managed Care Plans

If you have insurance, and it is not Medicare (traditional or Managed Care plan) or Medicaid, then you are probably on a Managed Care Plan. Managed Care Plans negotiate contracts with hospitals, doctors, and other healthcare providers. Each health plan has its own rules for how it pays. The hospital contracts separately and individually with each plan (or, in the case of aligned hospital organizations, together as a system). The plan may pay hospital "A" one way, using one rate, and pay hospital "B" on a completely different schedule. Some contracts may be based on DRGs, some on per diem (a rate per day of the stay), and sometimes they may even be based on charges (or as percentage of charges). The rules governing these selections are very complex and are well beyond the scope of this book.

Charity vs. Bad Debt

Patients who do not have any insurance may qualify for charity. In some cases, patients who *do* have insurance may still qualify for charity to cover a very large deductible. Each hospital has its own criteria for charity eligibility. If a patient qualifies for charity, no collection attempts are made. The patient's charges are simply written off without a bill ever being generated. Sometimes the hospital doesn't get the information to qualify a patient for charity until after a bill has been generated. In that case, the bill is written off and collection attempts are discontinued once the information is received.

Patients who do not qualify for charity are expected to pay their bill, or if they have insurance, are expected to pay their deductible and co-insurance amounts, if any. When a patient does not have a third party to pay for care, or if that third party requires a deductible or co-payment be made, the patient is expected to pay the bill or their portion of it. In the event of nonpayment, collection attempts will be made and will continue until either the debt is collected or the hospital gives up and writes off the account to bad debt.

Charity, then, relates to accounts written off because a patient did not have the ability to pay. *Bad Debt* relates to accounts written off because a patient who had the resources did not pay.

Denials

As we just discussed, when patients do not pay, the amount written off is called either bad debt or charity. But when an insurance company refuses to pay, it is called a *denial*.

The insurance (or managed care) company and the hospital sign a contract. The hospital agrees to provide care to the patients insured by the insurance company and on the amount they will accept as payment for those services. But, of course it would not be fair for the hospital to put patients in their beds who did not need care, just to collect the insurance money. For example, if you went to the emergency room with a twisted ankle, the hospital ER physician would take good care of you and send you home. He would not admit you to the hospital for three days because you don't need hospital inpatient-level care. And he shouldn't. And if he did, the insurance company would have every right to refuse to pay for anything beyond the care you received in the ER. If the hospital *did* admit you and *did* bill the insurance company, the result would be a denial of payment.

Denials are a reality; hospitals and insurance companies may have differing opinions about what care a patient needs. Denials may also be caused by a hospital or physician not getting an authorization in advance. By this point in your life either you, a friend, or a member of your family has certainly had surgery that was scheduled in advance, so you are familiar with your insurance company requiring an authorization in advance. They simply want to confirm that the surgery really is needed. Better to do that in advance, so no one is surprised after the fact.

WHY DOES ALL THIS MATTER TO YOU?

A long, long time ago—even before I was in healthcare finance—I suppose insurance companies may have paid hospitals whatever the billed charges were. I'm guessing that eventually these insurance companies began negotiating discounts with hospitals. In most cases, the discount was probably stated as a percentage of charges (say, 20%). So when a patient covered by that insurance plan received care, the hospital sent the insurance company an itemized bill, listing all charges from each department (nursing, pharmacy, surgery, lab, etc.). The insurance company then applied the 20% discount and sent the hospital a check. The difference between the amount of the charges (what we now call Gross Revenue), and the amount paid (what we now call Net Revenue), was referred to as Contractual Allowances (also shown as "Revenue Deductions"). It was an allowance for a discount that had been contractually negotiated. In those days, because every charge was reimbursed at a 20% discount, when you looked at the departmental financial statements, you knew exactly how much had been collected. It was 80% of whatever charges the department had generated.

Life is no longer this simple. Under the fixed reimbursement per patient or per diem arrangements, there is no accurate way to know what the collected revenues (net revenues) are for an individual department. Why? Let's have a look; here is an example.

A Medicare (DRG) patient is admitted to the hospital for a specific type of surgery. The payment to the hospital is fixed, based on "average" costs for that diagnosis (DRG). *(As a side note: Medicare uses compiled data from all Medicare hospitals to determine the average cost to care for a particular diagnosis—their*

DRG weights and payments are based on that information.) But what if the physician is uncomfortable and orders extra lab work, or perhaps additional x-rays? What if the patient has problems with anesthesia and stays in post-op longer than average—or cannot make arrangements in time to be discharged and so stays an extra day? All of these things increase charges in the affected departments *but do not change the revenue collected.* In some cases, the insurance company may even deny payment, or the account may be written off to bad debt or charity.

But assuming that payment is received, how would it be allocated among the departments? If it is allocated based on charges, then the surgery department, which stayed within the average, will now show less net revenue because more of the payment money is spread to the other departments for the extra services rendered. If you give surgery their 'expected" share, then perhaps some departments won't get allotted any of the money because the services they provided were not expected to be provided under a "normal" scenario. See how confusing and complicated it would be to allocate contractual allowances to each department?

Consequently, in most hospitals, when you look at an individual department's financial statements you will see Gross Revenues without any revenue deductions. The revenue deductions for the entire hospital will all be captured in the accounting department. Gross revenues without revenue deductions grossly overstates the financial performance of a revenue generating department! The difference between a hospital's gross charges and net revenues will vary but can be 70-80% different (i.e. the net revenues may be only 20-30% of the gross charges). If you really want to know what the true financial performance of your department is, ask your CFO what the hospital's overall ratio of net revenues to gross charges is. Then apply that percentage to your department's revenues. Compare that amount to the actual expenses of your department to see if your department has made a positive contribution to the hospital's financial performance.

Recap: If you want to see *true net revenues,* you can only see them by looking at the total hospital financial statement. It might look something like this:

Gross Revenues:	$1,000,000,000
Contractual Allowances:	$ 700,000,000
Charity	$ 50,000,000
Net Revenues	$ 250,000,000

In the example above, the ratio of net revenues to gross revenues is 25%. As we just discussed, because of the complexities of today's reimbursement models, hospitals do not "push" contractual adjustments down to the department level.

So, when you review your department's financial statement you may see this:

Department Gross Revenue $100,000
Department expenses: $ 50,000
Department Margin: **$ 50,000**

However, after talking with your CFO, you know the hospital Net Revenue, is (on average) 25% of gross charges. Now, let's revisit the performance of your department:

Department Gross Charges: $100,000
Estimated revenue deductions: $75,000
Estimated Net Revenue: **$25,000**
Department expenses: $50,000
Department Margin: **($25,000)**

Very different picture, huh?

Chapter 2 Self Review Questions

1. If the DRG payment for a diagnosis with a weight of 1.25 is $12,500, how much would the DRG payment be at the same hospital for a diagnosis with a CMI of 1.56?

2. If your hospital's variable cost per inpatient day is $1,800, and the DRG payment for a particular patient is $6,000, what is the hospital's margin if the patient stays 3 days? 5 days?

3. Two accounts were written off. One was written off to charity, and the other was written off to bad debt. Which account had collection efforts?

4. What is the difference between a denial and bad debt?

5. If your hospital's Gross Revenues were $29,773,615, Net Revenue was $12,359,123, and Contractual Allowances were $15,897,584, how much was written off to charity?

A Brief Accounting Lesson

Why is there a chapter in this book about accounting, when I promised not to talk to you about accounting? Well, there are a few accounting concepts you simply must understand if you are to manage intelligently and live up to your own accountability. But once you've read this short chapter, I'm sure you will feel that the pieces fit together a lot better. And when you have questions about your department financials you will be equipped to do research and ask pointed questions in an intelligent manner.

THE GENERAL LEDGER

General Ledger (or "G/L") is an accounting term. It refers to the old, pre-computer days when all accounting transactions were recorded in paper *ledgers*. There are ledgers for accounts receivable, accounts payable, etc. If you are still old fashioned enough to know what a checkbook and check register are, you could think of your check register as a cash ledger. Each ledger contains all the transactions related to those activities recorded in it (like a check register shows all checks written, ATM deposits and withdrawals etc.). The *General Ledger* is the ledger that all the other ledgers feed into; it is the "mother ship" so to speak.

At any point in time, the general ledger includes all the transactions and reflects the ending balances of every account in the ledger. There is an account for everything—or perhaps I should say, everything has an account to reflect its activity. The number of accounts in the G/L vary by company because each company has specific and differing needs, and they set up their accounts accordingly. An organization may have as many or as few accounts as they need. There are certain accounts that are required for accounting to "work," but that is beyond the scope of this book. For our purposes, you just need to understand that if you change jobs, your new employer's accounts *will* be different from those you saw with your previous employer. In today's accounting world, a G/L is a software application. You "post" entries into it.

The Chart of Accounts

Every company has its own list of accounts that they use in the G/L. This list is known as the *Chart of Accounts*. It may include thousands of accounts, but you needn't be concerned about most of them. You *will* want to obtain a copy of the section of the Chart of Accounts that includes the accounts that affect you, and that you *will* use. Your Finance Office can probably provide a relevant extract of accounts for you, or your intra-organizational website may have one posted. Ideally, you will want an account summary that includes definitions of the specific activities that are posted to each account. A fictitious excerpt from a chart of accounts is shown in **Exhibit 1,** in case you've never seen one. Let's take a quick look at it.

This fictitious chart of accounts excerpt comes from the Travel and Entertainment account. I've indented each level of detail.

See how all the accounts begin with a 9? That designates them as Travel and Entertainment accounts.

Then look at the first indentations. Those are 9010, 9020, 9030, etc. These are the sub-categories.

Finally, look at the third indentation. Within 9010, for example, you see 9010.10, 9010.20, 9010.30. These are the *actual* account numbers where activity is captured. Grouping things this way allows running reports that "roll-up" the detail. A report of everything captured in the 9000 accounts would include *all* the Travel and Entertainment accounts. A report of everything captured in the 9010 accounts would give only the details for Transportation. A report of everything in account 9010.10 would give only Plane Ticket expenses.

In addition to an account number that identifies the *type* of expense, the G/L account number will also include numbers to reflect the *department* where the activity occurred. Every department in the hospital has a number. You probably already know yours. For example, let's say the surgery department number is 2750. Using the fictitious chart

EXHIBIT 1			
Account #	Account Name		
9000.00	Travel and Entertainment		
	9010.00	Transportation	
		9010.10	Plane Tickets
		9010.20	Taxi expenses
		9010.30	Rental Cars
		9010.40	Milage reimbursement
		9010.50	Other Transportation
	9020.00	Lodging	
		9020.10	Hotel expenses
		9020.20	Other lodging expenses
	9030.00	Meals	
		9030.10	Meals out of town
		9030.20	Meals in town
		9030.30	Liquor
	9040.00	Other Expenses	
		9030.10	Entertainment

of accounts shown in **Exhibit 1,** if the surgery department wants to see only the hotel expenses associated with their department, then finance will run a report showing all activity in account 2750.9020.10. Notice that the account number is a *combination* of the department account number and the account number used to capture activity.

The Trial Balance

You may have heard the term Trial Balance. What is the difference between a *Chart of Accounts* and a *Trial Balance?* They are related, but they are two different things.

A Chart of Accounts is simply a listing of accounts used to post things into in the General Ledger.

The Trial Balance is actually a report run from the G/L that lists all the accounts in the Chart of Accounts, but then also shows *the total of all the activity* in those accounts.

Remember we said that the G/L is a software program? A Trial Balance is a report run out of the G/L software that does not show all the activity that has been posted, it only shows the ending balance of the account. Does that make sense?

Maybe an example will illustrate better. Imagine that three people from your department went to a seminar in a given budgeting period. Each had a plane ticket that cost $500. When each of those folks had to prepare an expense report, they would use the *Chart of Accounts* to see that plane tickets should be charged to account 9010.10. When they turned in those expense reports, the clerk in Accounts Payable would key into the computerized *General Ledger* to charge each of those $500 tickets to account 9010.10. At the end of the month, if you asked for a *Trial Balance* for your department, it would show that the activity in account 9010.10 totaled $1,500 ($500 per ticket x 3 people). If you could not remember what the expense was for, you could request the "G/L detail." The G/L detail would show you each of the three transactions (whereas the Trial Balance only showed you the total).

When you are given your department financial statements each month, they are probably summarized. You probably have four or five lines for expenses: salaries, supplies, maintenance and repairs, and then a catch-all line simply called "Other." Without any detail, it may be difficult to know what expenses are actually behind those summarized numbers—to be able to decipher your story. Having a Chart of Accounts helps you know what goes into each account. The Trial Balance and G/L detail available at the end of each month helps you get behind your numbers. We'll talk more about that later in the book.

Financial Reporting

As part of the G/L, the hospital will have a Financial Reporting function in the accounting software. This function is exactly what the name implies—*Financial Reporting*. It is used for nothing other than reporting of financial information.

When the system was initially set up and installed, someone sat down and designed, then defined which line of the financial statements each and every account would flow in to. By "lines" I am referring to things like "Gross Inpatient Revenues," "Salaries," "Supplies," etc., each being a *line* on the financial statements.

First they design (from scratch, or borrowing from a previous report) how the financial statements will look. What lines will they contain? For example, would the balance sheet only have one line to capture all fixed assets (simply called "Fixed Assets"), or would there be separate lines for "Buildings" and "Equipment" and then a line for "Total Fixed Assets?" Very basic, but important decisions.

After those decisions were made, they sat down with the chart of accounts and assigned each account to a line on the financial statements. For example, someone at one hospital may decide that account 8010.40 lawn maintenance (fictitious account number and name) would be grouped under the line called "Outside Services" because the service is performed by an *outside* service. Another hospital may not care who performs the service; they group it with "Maintenance and Repairs."

Why do I tell you this? You need to know so you can understand that it can vary a lot from one hospital to another. The accounts that one hospital refers to as "Other Expenses" may be completely different than another hospital. Even accounts that would seem like they would be reported the same, may vary across hospitals. It's all a matter of opinion. One hospital may consider hiring a DJ for the hospital employee Christmas party to be an employee relations expense, while another reports it as a purchased service.

Accountants live by a rule book called "Generally Accepted Accounting Principals" or "GAAP" (pronounced "gap"). This rule book says that all businesses who are required to report financial statements, have four of them:

1. Balance Sheet
2. Income statement (may go by various specific names)
3. Cash flow statement
4. Statement of changes in Equity (may also have various different names)

This book will only cover the Income Statement, but I thought you might find it useful to understand what the others are. Just in case you want to chat up your CFO sometime!

Balance Sheet: The balance sheet is a snapshot in time. That is the simplest way to think of it. It includes every single account in the G/L (summarized, of course). This is the mother of all financial statements. I say it is a snapshot in time because it only tells where everything stood at one exact moment in time. Think of it as if someone had a camera and "took a picture" of your business. Where everything stood at 11:59:59 on the last day of the fiscal year is what you see on the fiscal year end balance sheet—how much cash you had, receivables, what your total accounts payable balances were, what your debt was, and finally, what your net worth (or Equity) was.

The reason it is called a *Balance* sheet is that it . . . balances.

Assets = Liabilities + Equity.

If you remember that mathematical equations are communicative, then you can also look at this equation and rearrange it to say:

Assets + Liabilities = Equity.

That may make more sense to you. Either way, it all balances. The balance sheet will not be covered in this book.

Income statement: The income statement is the financial statement that this book will focus on. The difference between an income statement and a balance sheet is that:

1. The accounts contained in the income statement are a subset of the accounts contained on the balance sheet (remember the balance sheet includes all accounts), and

2. An income statement covers a PERIOD of time, not a MOMENT in time. An income statement covers a month, a year, etc. When you look at a number on an income statement, it reflects the sum of activity over time. (e.g., revenues are the total revenues earned over the period).

Cash Flow Statement: The cash flow statement will not be covered in this book. It is prepared to show the readers of the financial statements what caused the change in the cash balances from one balance sheet period to another. Say there were two balance sheets prepared; one as of March 31, 2009, and one prepared as of March 31, 2010. If the 2009 cash balance was $1,000,000, but had dropped to $100,000 by 2010, a curious reader may go look at the cash flow statement to see where the money went. Were there operational losses? Did the company generate revenue, but not collect the receivables? Was new capital equipment purchased? Were debts paid off? Perhaps a combination of all four. The important thing for you to understand is that an Income Statement is NOT a Cash Flow Statement! Your hospital's Income Statement may show what appears to you to be a "fat" bottom line, but unless you know what cash flow was, you cannot have any way of knowing whether the bottom line was enough to accomplish the objectives of the strategic plan or not. For example, the Income Statement does not include capital expenditures or debt. If your hospital's bottom line is small, or barely breaking even, then you are not generating enough money to invest in capital or pay down debt. In fact, you may be borrowing to subsidize capital or even cover payroll. When you think of your own personal expenses, you include your mortgage and other debt payments such as car loans and credit cards as "expenses". Accounting looks at those things differently. The Income Statement does not include any of those things. That is why it is important for a hospital to have a "healthy" bottom line–to have enough to cover all the cash needs not included in the Income Statement.

Statement of Changes in Equity: The statement of changes in Equity will not be covered in this book. If you hold stock in a company, this may be the most interesting financial statement to you. It details what transactions occurred that resulted in a change to the equity of a company. For a mature business, on a day-to-day basis, it is the profitability of the company that changes the equity values. With a Start-Up company, sales of stock and other transactions affect equity.

All these topics are beyond the scope of this book. But now you at least know the difference between one statement and the others.

Chapter 3 Self Review Questions

1. Does the Accounts Receivable Ledger feed into the General Ledger, or does the General Ledger feed into the Accounts Receivable Ledger?

2. If you needed to know what account number to use to charge a plane ticket to on your expense report, what document would you likely look at—the G/L, the TB, or the Chart of Accounts?

3. If your departmental operating statement showed an expense that you didn't recognize, and you wanted to investigate it, what report would you ask for from accounting?

4. If you were helping the CFO with a project, and were asked to find out what total Accounts Receivable were at June 30, 2008, what report would you want to review to find the answer to that question?

5. Your departmental operating statement is a subset of what financial report for your hospital?

Section II

Budgeting

CHAPTER 4

What is a Budget?

If you've been a manager for any length of time, I'm sure you have your own answer to that question already. And it may not be a nice answer. Let me see if I can help clarify.

Imagine you wanted to start your own business. Let's say it was going to be a coffee house. Unless you inherited a trust fund, you would probably need to convince someone to give or loan you some money to get started. Now, for just a moment, put yourself in the shoes of the potential lender or investor and think about all the questions you would want answered before you loaned or invested your money in this new venture:

- How much money do you need?

- What will that money pay for?

- Do you just want to open one coffee house, or a chain?

- Where will the first one be?

- How fast do you want to grow?

- Where will it—or they—be located? Why there?

- What will you serve?

- What will make you unique?

- How quickly will the first one open?

- How will you market yourself?

- When will I start seeing a return on my money?

- Over the long term, what kind of return will I get on my investment?

- How does that return compare to other options I have for investing my money?

Oh dear! You just wanted to open a coffee shop, and maybe—if it was successful—you could expand and open some more. Whew! How would you ever figure out the answers to all these questions? Actually, you probably already know the answers to many of them. They were part of the vision you saw when you came up with your idea. Now all you would need to do would be to put what you already know down on paper, and fill in the rest of the blanks.

When you first start a business, that process is called Building a Business Plan. Once you are up and running and hopefully growing (or deciding you want to grow), the process is called Building or Updating a Strategic Plan. Either way, you will (should) always have a plan for where you want to go next. Business Plans are typically five-year projections. Strategic plans can be longer or shorter in their projections, depending on what they indicate you will need. If the strategic plan involves a large and long project such as building a building, then the plan is usually longer-range.

Whether it's a Business Plan or a Strategic Plan, it will usually include all kinds of information about your vision:

- What do you want your business to look like five years from now?
- Do you want to have 100 shops open all over the country, or just one shop in your hometown?
- Who do you want to attract to your shop?
- How will you do that (poetry readings or wireless internet)?
- What are the demographics of that population?
- What is their discretionary income level (since your trying to sell a non-essential item)?
- Who is your competition in terms of your product?
- How close are they to you geographically?
- How are you going to be different from the competition?
- What other competition is there for your target demographic's purchasing dollars?

How might the answers to these questions change over time (e.g., if you're opening a single shop in your home town, what are the projections for your target population in five years; i.e., will it increase or decrease)?

I know, I know. You're wondering what in the world this has to do with a budget. I'm getting to that. Just stay with me.

So you figure out the answers to all those questions, and based on those answers, your idea probably changes a bit. Maybe you decide instead of just one shop on the downtown square in your home town, you decide that a better idea is three shops strategically placed around town—by the library, near the community college campus, and at the local shopping mall. Now you need to start putting details of the plan together. Hence, some new questions:

- All three shops at once, or one new shop a year over three years?

- Rent or buy real estate?

- How big will the shops be?

- What all equipment will you need—and should you rent or buy?

- How many staff will you need? What will you need to pay them? Are you going to offer them benefits? Can you afford to offer them benefits?

- How and when will you advertise?

- What hours will you be open?

- What prices will you charge for your menu items? What will your costs be?

- If you can't make a large enough profit on just selling coffee, what else can you sell, and how profitable will those items be?

Do you notice anything all of these questions have in common? Yes, it's money. The answers to all these questions will drive how much money you need and when it will be required to implement your plans.

NOW you're ready to pull it all together. Your decisions:

- One shop per year for three years.

- Rent space.

- Small, intimate shops, selling a unique coffee blend you have licensed exclusively in your city, with cookies and pastries to the 18-24 year old age group.

- You'll be cheaper than Starbucks, but more upscale than McDonalds.

- Right now, there is no competition for that in-between market.

- Wireless Internet as well as a wide variety of newspapers, overhead music, and paintings from local artists looking to sell (so no cost to you).

- Four to six month to open the first shop, sales slowly growing during first year, at capacity by end of third year.

Putting this on paper will translate into your Business Plan.

The Business Plan will have a section for *financial projections* including the pre-opening expenses, then the expected costs in excess of revenues when the shop initially opens, ramping up to capacity in year three when the profit margins are satisfactory to attract financing.

So finally you find someone to finance you, and you're off and running. But your investor wants to monitor his money. He wants to know if you are on track. How does he do that? Simple. He takes the financial projections you did for each year and lets you know he wants to measure you against them at the end of each month. At the end of year one, if things are on track, your financial performance should be similar to your financial projections. The financial results tell him if you are on track.

If so, let's think about whether or not you should perhaps tweak year two up a notch? Accelerate the other two store openings?

If you are significantly below first year projections, look at the new questions that need answering:

- What adjustments need to be made to year two?

- Is growth slower? Did it take longer to get the store open and established than you originally thought?

- Will you run out of money?

- Is your middle-ground pricing strategy working?

- Have you attracted quality staff at the wages you expected?

- Did you end up spending more on benefits than you thought?

All these things will have an impact on whether or not your investor is going to realize the return on investment that he anticipated when he agreed to fund your new venture.

Did it click yet? Do you see the connection between my story and the name of this chapter? **That's what the budget is.**

It's the business plan or strategic plan sliced into one-year pieces. It tells what you want to achieve that year—what you need to achieve in order to stay on track with your long range goals and vision. And the one-year plan is then sliced into 12 pieces, one for each month. That way you can look at things in a more timely way. If the plan was to open the shop in month five, there were assumptions you had to make around that. So if that didn't happen, other things are affected.

Make sense? Now let's apply these same concepts to a hospital.

Let's assume your hospital has a recently prepared strategic plan. It's time to start preparing the budget for next year. You're in charge. Don't worry—you'll do great! But how do you know where to start?

The good news is that you probably have a great budget tool that will help you answer this question. It's your budget software. And if you're lucky, you have a person on staff who specializes in using this software. This person can tell you everything you'll need to know in order to input into the software to run the budget. And guess what? Much of the information you need to input was already developed when the strategic plan was prepared. So that's a great place to start!

Remember, the budget for next year is going to be the next 12-month slice of your strategic plan. It will be more detailed, so there will be some questions you'll need answered that aren't in the strategic plan. Additionally, remember, some things have probably changed such that there needs to be a few tweaks. For example, let's say that your strategic plan called for expansion of your Operating Room suites. That expansion was to be completed in year two. You are now preparing the budget to go with year three of the strategic plan, but there were construction delays and the OR expansion will not be finished until mid year next year. So the increased OR capacity and volume that was built in to the strategic plan for year three will not begin until mid-year. This is an example of a "tweak" or adjustment that needs to be made between the strategic plan and the budget.

So now you're nervous again? Wondering how you would ever know everything you need to consider? Don't panic. There are three sets of questions you need answered to get started on the budget:

1. What assumptions in the strategic plan can be confirmed to stand as-is?

2. What assumptions in the strategic plan need to be tweaked or adjusted?

3. What additional details are there that exist at a more granular level than the strategic plan? An example would be that the strategic plan probably has assumptions about overall hospital volumes, but now you will need to decide how that volume will be spread among the various Nursing units.

What? You don't know all these answers? Not to worry! What does a good manager do when they need answers to questions? Have a meeting!

A well planned budget will always begin with a budget planning meeting to discuss these three sets of questions. At the very least, this meeting will be attended by the C-suite (CEO, COO, CNO, and usually led by the CFO), but may include other attendees as well. Let's pretend for a moment that you are the CFO and you are in charge of the budget this year, so you will lead this meeting. Here are some questions you will want to be sure and discuss:

1. How many patients do we expect to care for next year compared to this year? Why do we think the number will be different? Are we full now, but adding capacity, or do we have excess capacity but our population is growing?

2. If the number is more or less than this year, what areas of the hospital do we expect those changes to affect? Nursing units? Surgery? Emergency room?

3. How long (on average) do we expect the inpatients to stay? Do we have any initiatives planned that will increase or decrease this length of stay?

4. What services do we expect these patients to need while they are here?

5. How much do we plan to charge for these services?

6. How much do we expect to be paid for these services? Are there any issues with our payors we need to build into the budget?

7. What resources will we need to care for these patients?

8. Are there any plans to modify any staffing ratios or staffing matrices?

9. Are there any plans to add or discontinue any services?

10. What inflation is expected on supplies and other externally purchased services?

11. Are there any external factors that need to be considered (e.g. labor union activity)?

12. Are there any internal changes being considered such as changes to benefit plans?

13. Will merit raises be given? If so, when, and how much?

14. What turnover is expected compared to current year, and what impact do we expect that to have on recruiting, hiring and training new staff?

As you can imagine, this list of questions could go on for the remainder of this book! And the questions probably will continue as the budget is prepared. No, we are not going to address all these questions in this book. The reason I illustrated some of them is again to drive home the point that the budget is merely a *plan for operations* for the coming 12-month period. It is that plan translated into numbers (finance-ese). If you can understand finance-ese, when you look at a budget, you will see the answers to these and many other questions that a board member, a CEO, a bank or loan officer, or an investor might have.

THE FIRST THING THE CFO DOES

While everyone else may be talking about the strategic plan as it relates to next year's budget and what they're going to ask for in the capital budget, every good CFO is behind closed doors figuring out what I call the baseline forecast. It gives him a starting point for the budget. Depending on your hospital, this baseline may be only an operating budget baseline, or it may include capital, too, and be a cash flow budget.

Just as you had to answer to your coffee shop investor, whether your hospital is public or private, for-profit or not-for-profit, there is a good chance that it has banks (lien holders on debt), shareholders, or investors to answer to. Any or all of these stakeholders probably have established minimum financial requirements that the hospital must meet or maintain, such as a specific financial performance or a certain amount of cash in the bank. Building a budget that meets those criteria is the CFO's job. So before the budget process starts, and all the while that it's going on, he is preparing and updating a little one-page document he prepared.

The initial baseline forecast (*Example shown in* **Exhibit 2** *below*) is the CFO's best estimate of what the financial performance next year would look like with no intervention. He combines what he knows will happen with his

Row/Col	(numbers in 000's)	A	B	C	D	E	F
		EXHIBIT 2					
		J Lee Community Hospital					
		Baseline Forecast - FY 2012					
		YTD Actual Thru 8 months	Projected 4 months	Total CY Projection	Inflation	Other Changes	FY 2012 Forecast
1	Net Patient revenues	$300,000	$150,000	$450,000	$4,500	$(15,000)	$439,500
2	Other operating Revenues	$400	$200	$600	$-	$(100)	$500
3	Total Net Revenues	$300,400	$150,200	$450,600	$4,500	$(15,100)	$440,000
4							
5	Salaries	$120,000	$60,000	$180,000	$5,400	$(7,500)	$177,900
6	Contract labor	$10,000	$5,000	$15,000	$(3,750)	$-	$11,250
7	Benefits	$24,000	$12,000	$36,000	$3,600	$-	$39,600
8	Supplies	$62,500	$31,250	$93,750	$1,875	$(3,000)	$92,625
9	Maintenance & Repairs	$400	$200	$600	$12	$500	$1,112
10	Other expenses	$30,000	$15,000	$45,000	$900	$-	$45,900
11	Depreciation	$17,000	$8,500	$25,500	$-	$-	$25,500
12	Amortization	$10,000	$5,000	$15,000	$-	$-	$15,000
13	Interest expense	$11,000	$5,500	$16,500	$-	$-	$16,500
14	Bad Debt	$15,000	$7,500	$22,500	$-	$-	$22,500
15	Total Operating Expenses	$299,900	$149,950	$449,850	$8,037	$(10,000)	$447,887
16							
17	Income from operations	$500	$250	$750	$(3,537)	$(5,100)	$(7,887)
18	Investment Income	$6,300	$3,150	$9,450	$-	$-	$9,450
19	Income before taxes	$6,800	$3,400	$10,200	$(3,537)	$(5,100)	$1,563
20							
21	Add back non-cash expenses:						
22	Depreciation & Amortization	$27,000	$13,500	$40,500			$40,500
23	= Cash flow from operations	$33,800	$16,900	$50,700			$50,700
24	Less Capex	$(50,000)	$(10,000)	$(60,000)			$(60,000)
25	= Net Cash flow this year	$(16,200)	$6,900	$(9,300)			$(9,300)
26	Add Cash balance at beginning of period	$750,000	$733,800	$750,000			$740,700
27	= Ending Cash	$733,800	$740,700	$740,700			$731,400

best guesses. Those guesses solidify over the course of the budget preparation. This forecast allows him to monitor whether or not next year's budget is shaping up to meet the lender/investor's financial requirements.

Exhibit 2 *(page 37)* shows a simple example baseline forecast. Here are the assumptions the CFO made when this baseline was built:

1. *Columns A through C* start out with year-to-date (YTD) actual numbers and add a best guess for the remaining months to determine how the current fiscal year (FY) is going to turn out. Remember, budget planning will likely start when there are 3-6 months remaining in the current year.

2. *Column D* adds estimated overall factors for inflation and merit raises.

3. *Column E* adds or takes away things he knows will happen. Say, for example, a Nursing unit is going to be closed for renovation starting at the beginning of the new FY, and be closed for 5 months. As shown here, the CFO has estimated that loss of those beds for 5 months will reduce revenues by $15 million *(row 1 column E)*, but will also reduce labor and supply costs by $6.5 million and $3 *(row 8 column E)* million respectively. Maybe your hospital installed some large IT systems last year. Next year the excess labor costs will go away, but a new maintenance contract will be added. So you see labor is decreased again by another $1 million (for a total reduction in labor of $7.5 million—*row 5 column E*), but maintenance expense is increased by $500,000 *(row 9 column E)*. Another example would be estimates for known reimbursement changes. Perhaps your hospital receives $100,000 in grant funds that are drying up. Since this money is not considered Patient Care revenues, I've shown it on the "Other Operating Revenues" *(row 2 column E)* line. Another example not shown here might be if your hospital is a public hospital and you expect tax revenues to increase. This column captures all of these types of events.

4. *Column F* then shows what the next FY operating statement will look like if all and only these things "come true."

Now step back and look at the results of this analysis. Look at the Income from Operations Line *(row 17)*. Ouch! If nothing changes, the hospital will go from making $750,000 *(row 17 column C)* to losing $7,887,000 *(row 17 column F)*! Ending cash balances will decrease by $9.3 Million *(row 25 column F)*.

Now you can understand why the CFO prepares this schedule at the beginning of the budget process. If your hospital does have financial requirements, and if *column F* does not meet those requirements, then discussions will likely begin around what things will need to happen to achieve the required performance. It's much better to know this and make these decisions early on than to prepare the budget and get to the end, only to find out you must start over because the budget will not meet required criteria.

I know, I am really trying not to bore you with things that don't affect you, but although this schedule isn't something you will participate in preparing, knowing that this is going on behind the scenes may help you understand why you hear comments during the budget preparation like, "We may have to reduce or delay merit raises next year," or, "We may need to restructure benefit plans next year to reduce the costs." Or worse yet, you are told you will need to reduce the expenses in your department.

I'm sure you've heard some version these statements from your own CFO. Maybe you wondered how they could know this early in the preparation period that these things were going to need to be done. Now you know!

Chapter 4 Self Review Questions

1. What is the difference between a Business Plan and a Strategic Plan?

2. What is the connection between a Strategic Plan and a Budget?

3. True or False: A Strategic Plan does not need to be updated every year.

4. Which of the following questions would you expect to hear a CFO discussing at the annual budget planning meeting?

   a. How many patients do we expect to care for next year compared to this year?

   b. Are there any plans to add or discontinue services?

   c. Are there any plans to make changes to the employee benefit plans?

   d. All of the above.

5. Using the example in **Exhibit 2**, what was the expected impact of inflation on next year's Income from Operations?

Capital Budgets and Expenses vs. Operating Budgets and Expenses

Now that you understand what a budget is, there are several kinds of them. The three main ones are *operating budgets, capital budgets,* and *cash flow budgets.*

The cash flow budget is actually a marriage of the capital and operating budgets. It combines them to answer the ultimate questions we finance folks like to know, questions like: what will happen to my cash balances this year? Will I have enough to pay my people? My vendors? Buy the things I need to run my business (and hopefully grow it)? If I want to buy a piece of equipment, do I need to borrow some money to do that, or will I have enough in the bank to cover it?

Answering those questions though, clearly is not a part of your job. The two budgets we're going to look at in this book are the two you, as a manager, deal with: Capital and Operating.

The purpose of the budget process is to translate all your planning assumptions into dollar terms. If things go as you plan, how much money will come in, and how much money will go out? And every penny that comes in or goes out is associated with one of the two budgets—capital or operating. Let me say that again:

"Every penny that comes in or goes out during the year is either capital or operating. Every single penny."

Capital money doesn't come in, it only goes out. So money coming in is always operating. Money that goes out can be either—but it is always one of the two.

So while you're making your list of things you want to spend money on during the year, you could (quite literally) take a pad of paper and divide it into two columns. Every penny you want to spend must go in one of the two columns.

So what goes in which column? And why?

To answer that, let's back up a minute and talk a bit about accounting. We accountants like everything to be neat and tidy. But it has to also make sense. Capital spending was a way we made something that was neat and tidy also make sense.

Let me explain. Sometimes you may hear people who own small businesses talk about keeping their books on a "cash basis." That means that everything is recorded in the period it is paid. No matter what. So, let's say you own your coffee shop, and since you have no established credit as a business owner, the landlord requires you to pay a whole year of rent up front. If you were using "cash basis" accounting, then you would record all of that expense all in the month you paid it, and then not have rent expense show up again in the numbers for the next eleven months. If your investor wants to see how you were doing and asks what your bottom line is for that month, things would look a little lopsided, wouldn't they? You'd have one month of cash receipts for coffee and pastry sales, but you'd have 12-months of rent expense. We accountants don't think that is very neat and tidy. We like things to match.

Since the landlord wasn't *earning* his rent from you until you actually occupied the space each month, you hadn't really incurred the expense yet. So for cash flow purposes, it was cash-out, but for accrual accounting purposes, you would spread out recording the expense—recognizing one-twelfth of it each month. As a side note, you would record the rest of the money you paid out as a Pre-paid expense. It would be an asset that in a simple, non-legal world, you could turn back into cash in the form of a refund if you moved out (think of an apartment deposit—same idea). Revenue works the same way.

Aaaahhhhh . . . did you feel it? You just learned accounting. What I just described is Accrual accounting. You put revenues and expenses together in the period you earned (revenue) or incurred (expenses) them, no matter when you collected or paid them. In healthcare, hospitals usually get paid anywhere from two weeks to up to two years after they provide care or services to a patient. But the revenue is recorded in the month the services were provided (so the money was earned), and the expenses incurred (salaries, benefits, supplies, etc.) are recorded in the period they were incurred, regardless of when the money is collected or the expenses were paid. That's the matching concept behind accrual accounting. That way you can tell whether or not what you are doing is profitable or not. The Cash Flow statement described in **Chapter 3** is used to show if you are collecting cash and paying bills timely.

So you think you're ready to go take the CPA exam now? Not intimidated by your CFO anymore? Might want to wait a few more minutes. Remember, we still have to get to explaining capital vs. operating expenses. We just got a little sidetracked talking about cash vs. accrual accounting. But there was a method to my madness. Calling something a capital expense is the same concept as deciding to record something on the accrual basis, except that it applies only in certain situations.

Let's use an example that is so large that it's obvious. If you work in a hospital, you know what an MRI machine is. It's a very expensive piece of equipment. For discussion purposes, let's assume it costs $3 million. Thinking back to the pre-paid rent issue, it's easy to see that for accounting purposes, we want to spread the cost of the equipment over some period of time. Right?

Just in case it's not so obvious, Look at **Exhibit 3**. Imagine you did not spread the cost out, but expensed the entire machine the month you bought it. Let's say you collect $1,000 for each scan, and you did 1,000 scans the year you bought it—earning you $1,000,000 in revenue. But if you expense the entire machine that month, with $1,000,000 in revenue, and $3,000,000 in expenses, your investors won't be happy. But then next year, let's say you do 1,000 scans again, earning $1,000,000 again—but now you have no expense. Great financial performance, but not really an accurate picture is it? Why not? Because you used the machine to earn the revenue—so there should be an expense associated with that. And using the machine reduces it's value (like driving a car reduces a car's value). The accountants are twitching. It doesn't feel right. How can we make it neat and tidy and make sense?

If you continued to run 1,000 scans a year, eventually, after 5 years, your revenues would be $5 million in total, and you would have earned $3,750,000 on your $3 million investment giving you a $750,000 return on your investment, but the accounting for all of the individual years would be mis-stated because you didn't match the expense with the revenue.

EXHIBIT 3						
	Treat as Operating Expense					
	Year 1	Year 2	Year 3	Year 4	Year 5	Total
Net revenue	$1,000,000	$1,000,000	$1,000,000	$1,000,000	$1,000,000	$5,000,000
Salaries	$200,000	$200,000	$200,000	$200,000	$200,000	$1,000,000
Supplies	$50,000	$50,000	$50,000	$50,000	$50,000	$250,000
Cost of Capital	$3,000,000	$-	$-	$-	$-	$3,000,000
Total expenses	$3,250,000	$250,000	$250,000	$250,000	$250,000	$4,250,000
Operating Income	$(2,250,000)	$750,000	$750,000	$750,000	$750,000	$750,000

Accountants don't like that, so we came up with a way to fix it. You know what I'm getting ready to say, don't you? That's right . . . *depreciation.* You know, that thing you never have to mess with, that no one asks you about, that you don't have to budget for because someone in Accounting does it for you.

Depreciation is a way to spread cost over the time the equipment will be used—its useful life—which also (not coincidentally) then is a way to expense the reduction in value that occurs each time the equipment is used. See how that works? Accountants are clever that way. Kill two birds with one stone. Look at **Exhibit 4** *(next page)*. Exact same scenario as **Exhibit 3,** but now we've

	Treat as Capital Expense					
EXHIBIT 4						
	Year 1	Year 2	Year 3	Year 4	Year 5	Total
Net Revenue	$1,000,000	$1,000,000	$1,000,000	$1,000,000	$1,000,000	$5,000,000
Salaries	$200,000	$200,000	$200,000	$200,000	$200,000	$1,000,000
Supplies	$50,000	$50,000	$50,000	$50,000	$50,000	$250,000
Cost of Capital	$600,000	$600,000	$600,000	$600,000	$600,000	$3,000,000
Total Expenses	$850,000	$850,000	$850,000	$850,000	$850,000	$4,250,000
Operating Income	$150,000	$150,000	$150,000	$150,000	$150,000	$750,000

used depreciation. The 5-year totals are the exact same, but the individual years are much more balanced, and reflective of the revenues earned, and the resources utilized to earn the revenues.

Since you never have to mess with depreciation, you're wondering why I'm bringing it up, especially since I promised to talk only—or mostly—about things that mattered to you in this book. Right? Well, I do have a reason. Because *depreciation is something that only happens to capital items.* So if you want to buy something that seems like it should have its cost spread over an extended period of time using depreciation, then you're probably wanting to buy something that needs to go into your capital budget.

CAPITAL POLICIES

How do you know whether or not your company believes the item you want to buy is a capital or operating item? Remember the rule that every penny must be either capital or operating? The easiest thing to do is to determine whether or not the item is capital first, and if it isn't, then by default it must be operating. But you need to know this: It is a completely subjective view. Every company has its own policy. In a completely idealistic world, the policy is based on "materiality." That's an accounting term. In simple terms, it means that the cost is big enough that expensing it all at once would misstate the financial statements. Okay, so a $3 million piece of equipment is capital. That's easy. But not everything is so obvious. And it can change when you change employers. What about a computer? Or a desk? These items may be capital at one company but an operating expense at another. How are you to know? You will need to read the company policy.

When you see your company's capital policy, it will most likely have four criteria:

1. It must be a tangible asset. That means it must be something you can touch and see.

And . . .

2. The item must cost more than $XXX. How big or small $XXX is will vary by company, based on what is "material" to them. A multi-billion dollar bank will lose the cost of a laptop computer in rounding (literally), whereas at your coffee shop, that laptop may be a very large purchase.

Or . . .

3. If there is a group of items that must be purchased together, even though the cost of individual pieces is less than $XXX, if the total price exceeds $YYY, then the capital criteria is met.

And . . .

4. The item must have a useful life of more than a year. Think about that. If the item will be "used up" within the year, then it's not worth the hassle of tracking it.

Notice that items 1 and 3 have an *"and"* after them, while item 2 has an *"or"* after it. So when deciding whether or not something is capital, it *must* meet criteria 1 and 4, but it only needs to meet either criterion 2 or criterion 3.

Let's look at some examples. To make it fun, let's use personal items. The lesson is the same.

Imagine you are one of us nerdy accountants and keep personal financial statements. Pretend you are preparing a budget for next year. Below is a list of things you anticipate you will buy. Which of the items would you consider to be capital, and which would be operating (remember—everything must be one or the other)?

a. A new home

b. A new car

c. Groceries

d. $10,000 of new clothes

e. Resetting your (or your wife's) engagement ring with a new 10th year anniversary diamond

f. Vacation expenses

g. A new roof on the house because there is a leak

h. A new water heater

i. A used car for your son

j. A 3 year membership to a health club

Write down your answers on a piece of paper before you peek at the answers below.

Done? OK, let's look at each item. It's important to remember that answers may vary from person to person, depending on that person's definition of "materiality." At the end of the day, the "DC" (Denise Chamberlain) definition of capital is this: "If you still have something left at the end of a year, it's probably capital. But accounting for (tracking) capital is a hassle, so you decide if it's big enough to be worth the hassle of tracking it." Based on that definition, let's look and see whether or not I would consider these items *Capital* or *Operating:*

a. A new home—probably *capital* by anyone's definition.

b. A new car—probably also *capital* by most "regular" folks definitions. Even if you're really rich, you probably buy really expensive cars, so a new car is probably capital.

c. Groceries—*Operating.* Groceries don't meet the DC acid test "if you have something left at the end of a year." Nor do they meet the materiality threshold.

d. $10,000 of new clothes—*this depends what you buy, and what your materiality threshold is.* If you buy 3 suits at $2,000 each and 3 pairs of shoes at $1,300 each, and plan to keep them forever, then they would be capital. But if you are a celebrity, and this money is for 1 outfit for the Oscars, and you'll never wear it again, it's Operating. If you spend $10,000 on t-shirts, shorts and flip-flops for your 5 children, and the clothes will be outgrown or worn out by yearend, then it's operating.

e. Re-setting the engagement ring—Probably *capital* in most "regular" folks books.

f. Vacation expenses—clearly *operating expenses.*

g. A new roof because there is a leak—split decision here again—probably *capital* for you as an individual homeowner, but it COULD be *operating* for a business. If you work in Facilities and need more info on this, see your CFO.

h. A new water heater—for this item, I would refer to the *DC (Denise Chamberlain) rule.* Yes, you have something that will last more than a year, but whether or not the price is worth the hassle to you of tracking and depreciating it, is up to you.

i. A used car for your son—this is also an item left to your discretion. If you go buy an old clunker for $200 that he's going to fix up, but you anticipate will be wrecked in a year, then it's probably an *operating* expense. If you spend a "material" amount of money, and expect him to drive it for several years, then it's probably capital for most "regular" folks.

j. A three-year membership to a gym—this was the trick question. You are probably thinking the answer depends on the price and whether or not it's "material," but the truth is, it doesn't matter. Remember rule #1 of the definition of capital? It must be a *tangible* asset that you can see and touch. A gym membership is not that, so no matter how long it lasts, or how much it costs, it is *not* a capital asset.

Wow! Wasn't that exciting? Aren't you ready to just run out and buy some financial software and start tracking your own personal financial statements?

Oh, that's right—I forgot. You aren't a nerdy accountant. But at least you are more comfortable now that you know the difference between operating and capital expenses.

Chapter 5 Self Review Questions

1. If a dollar spent is not Operating or Capital, what is it?

2. Is depreciation expense an Operating expense or a Capital expense?

3. Which of the following is NOT a requirement for an item to be considered Capital?

   a. It must be a tangible asset

   b. It must have a useful life greater than one year

   c. It must cost a large sum of money

   d. All of the above are requirements for an item to be considered Capital.

4. If a gym membership lasts 3 years, and costs a lot of money, is it Capital?

5. Is a family vacation a Capital or an Operating expense?

Strategic Initiative and Capital Requests and Justifications

When you're in the planning stage of the coming year's budget, the very first place you start is by looking at what initiatives you want to implement. Just as the general budget has two big categories—operating and capital—the operating budget is actually a combination of two sets of assumptions:

1) those associated with your recurring services and operations, and

2) those associated with changes you want to make (i.e. Initiatives).

Remember the connection between the budget and the strategic plan or business plan? The budget is simply a one-year piece of your strategic plan, cut into 12 slices, one for each month. So before you can start the budget, you need to revisit that plan and see what things need to go into this year's budget. It may be new things and/or removal of old things, like shutting down a service. Go back to **Exhibit 2** *(page 37)*. Remember the column for "Other Changes?" That is what this chapter is about: figuring out what changes in operations are going to happen (or you *want* to happen) compared to current operations.

When you revisit the strategic plan, it may turn out that the plan needs updating. Or when your CFO prepares the Baseline forecast, it may indicate that changes *must* be made in order to achieve the desired financial results. You may or may not be involved in that process. Or instead of participating in updating the plan, you may have the opportunity to make your own suggestions or requests. Or as part of a request for capital funds, you may need to prepare a short document justifying the capital. All of these things follow a very similar process. Some will involve many departments, over several years (such as a construction project), and some may be very small, such as justifying a small capital item. For purposes of this book, I will call them all *Strategic Initiatives* (whether they are *capital* or *operating* in nature).

I'm sure you're quite aware there is never enough money to approve even one fourth of all the strategic initiative capital requests everyone wants to make, or to implement the new programs they want. Choices must be made.

The best way for you to have the greatest chance of success for getting the things *you* want is to be able to clearly and succinctly justify that your request is, in fact, the best use of the funds you are asking for. One very important thing to remember is that *the people making the decisions may know very little about your clinical affairs.* You think understanding finance is difficult, yes? Well, they feel the same way about understanding what you do. So the simpler you can make your justification, the better. Also, it helps to remember that finance folks are very logical, and sequential thinkers.

Where to start? The first thing you need to know, if you are new in your position and haven't done a budget with your current company before, is exactly what your responsibilities are regarding strategic initiatives. If you are responsible for any, as I mentioned, the process will be very similar whether you are justifying a small sum of money for a capital item for your department or large sums of money to renovate space, hire staff, buy equipment, or begin marketing a new service.

Your company will probably have a standard form (or set of forms) for you to prepare. Some may be longer or more sophisticated than others. The sample form we will walk through here should be representative of most of what you as a manager need to understand. If your company has forms or processes more complicated than this, the good news is that the finance folks will probably be helping you with the more complicated parts!

Review the sample blank form shown in **Exhibit 5**, and let's go down the form row by row. In my example, the gray shaded box is for the accounting folks to use, so you needn't worry about it.

1. **FY Ending:** This is the year that the last month of your company's fiscal year ("FY") falls in. Many hospitals do not observe a December 31 year-end for their fiscal year. Which means the fiscal year will start in one calendar year, and end in the next calendar year. Let's use a June 30 fiscal year end as an example. If the year starts July 1, 2010, then it ends June 30, 2011. That would be fiscal year 2011. So if you are requesting money for that fiscal year, even if you plan to spend the money in September 2010, your request is a *FY2011* request.

2. **Department:** In most cases, the request will only affect one department—yours.

3. **Name of Request:** This should be a description of the request that is specific enough, yet short enough to be used throughout the approval process when referring to the request. You should be as descriptive as possible. Words like "New Equipment" are too vague. Even words like "MRI" are too vague. Are you requesting a new MRI? An upgrade to an existing machine? A second machine?

EXHIBIT 5		
J Lee Community Hospital **Budget Request**	Budget Dept Use Only	Request #_____
	Approved?	Y N
Fiscal Year Ending		20_____
Department Name		
Name of Request		
Total Money Requested:		
Operating Funds		$
Capital Funds		$
Capital Requests only:		
Fiscal quarter funds are needed (circle one)		1 2 3 4
Priority rating (A = Mandatory, B = Urgent, C = Needed but not urgent)		A B C
Is this request associated with compliance with a new regulatory requirement?		Y N
Is this request associated with compliance with an existing but deficient regulatory requirement?		Y N
Describe your request		
Describe the benefits to the hospital of granting your request		
Describe the risks to the hospital if your request is not granted		
Will granting your request increase Net Revenues?		Y N
If so, how much per month (detail needs to be attached)?		$
If so, what month will revenues begin?		J F M A M J J A S O N D
Will granting your request increase expenses?		Y N
If so, how much per month (detail needs to be attached)?		$
If so, what month will expenses begin?		J F M A M J J A S O N D
Will granting your request require additional FTEs to be hired?		Y N
If so, how many?		
If so, what month will the increase begin?		J F M A M J J A S O N D
Does this request have IT implications (hardware/software/interfaces/training)?		Y N
Prepared by (printed name)		
Submitted by (Director Signature)		
Date submitted		

4. **Operating Funds Requested:** You may need some help with this from finance, depending on how complicated the request is. For now, let's talk about a few simple examples. If you are requesting a new piece of capital equipment (something the hospital does not currently have), you will need to check warranty terms with the vendor and, if needed, the cost of a maintenance contract. That expense will not be capital but will be a recurring operating expense each year. If you are buying a piece of used equipment, the same is true. Some more complicated examples include situations such as a piece of equipment being added that will require expenses for staff and supplies but will also generate revenue.

5. **Capital Funds Requested:** This is the *total* amount of money required to bring the asset(s) on stream. *Get a quote from the vendor before submitting your capital funding request.* Also, remember to make sure the quoted price will still be good when you are ready to purchase. For example: if you are requesting the money for 4th quarter, your quote from the vendor needs to be good for 9-12-months. Other questions to consider when determining the total amount of funds you need for a particular project/asset:

   a. Does the vendor quote include tax and freight, or do those need to be added? (Finance can help with that.)

   b. Are there going to be costs to install the equipment?

   c. Are there space renovations required?

   d. Will the item will be used in conjunction with a computer? If so, will new computers be required? Will an interface need to be written?

6. **Fiscal Quarter Needed:** Everyone would like to buy everything right away. Of course that isn't possible. Depending on the hospital's cash reserve levels, it may be that no money is available until it is generated that year through profits or positive cash flow. To illustrate, let's say your hospital has zero cash reserves (Yikes!). If the budget is for $1 million of cash to be generated first quarter, then perhaps, the $1 million you need to purchase your equipment will have to wait until after the money is generated. Which means you would have to wait until at least 2nd quarter. As a manager, I would recommend you put as many of your requests as possible for the first quarter. Finance will most likely push many of them back to later quarters. But if you don't ask for the money until 4th quarter, I promise you that no one is going to contact you to ask if you'd like it sooner! Try to avoid 4th quarter money. Many times if the financial performance isn't going as well as planned, or if other emergencies arise during the year, the money budgeted for capital in the 4th quarter may well get taken away. Also, if you miss getting the goods

actually delivered by the last day of the fiscal year, you may lose the money, and not be able to get it back.

7. **Priority Rating (A B or C):** This is a way for management to determine which projects will get funded when there isn't enough money to buy everything. Many hospitals have ratings such as these.

   *Ranking "A":** In many hospitals, only absolute "must haves" can be ranked an A. These are usually one of two types: 1) The hospital has a regulatory deficiency now, or a new regulation is coming in to effect that the hospital is not compliant with, or 2) There is a project from last year that is incomplete, and funds must be allocated to complete or continue it (e.g., a construction project).

   *Ranking "B":** This is where most other requests that get approved will fall. These are items that are very important, but do not meet the criteria to be ranked an A.

   *Ranking "C":** Projects ranked "C" are not urgent, and thus are the first to get cut when there aren't enough funds to cover everything. If capital funding is tight in a given year, management may give directives for staff not to submit Priority C items. If that happens to you, don't take offense. Management is actually trying to help you by not having you waste precious time gathering data and preparing a request that they already know they will not be able to fund.

8. **Regulatory Compliance:** These questions are asked to highlight funding requests associated with new or existing regulatory compliance issues. Some hospitals may extend these questions to include issues that are not related to specific regulatory codes but are a patient safety issue.

9. **Describe your request:** Here is your chance to "sell your story." Take this opportunity to explain what your request is. To the extent possible, do it in lay terms; remember that the folks reading it may well not understand anything clinical.

10. **Describe the benefit to the hospital of granting your request:** Here is an even better opportunity to sell your story. What are the benefits? Is it fixing a patient safety issue? Will it bring in more patients? Will it make the hospital more efficient? Will it reduce expenses? Will it address an issue that is giving the hospital a bad image? Will it allow the hospital to do something it cannot do right now? All of these and more are benefits to the hospital of acquiring capital or undertaking a project. To sell your idea, you need to be able to clearly describe in detail what these benefits are. Remember: they don't have to be financial.

11. **Describe the risk to the hospital if your request is not granted:** This is just the opposite of the section above. Maybe the money is needed for a defensive strategy—to stop something bad from happening.

12. **Will granting your request increase Net Revenues?:** If so, how much and when will they begin? You may need some help from finance to answer this. Remember that the question is whether or not it will increase net revenues. Everything you charge for generates gross revenues, but not all gross revenues generate net revenue (which means cash). Many requests do not generate any revenue. A request for marketing, or to increase nursing ratios, or to buy software to better manage something—none of these requests would generate any gross revenue. Some requests may generate gross revenue but no net revenue. Finance can help you with this. For example, if most of your payors pay you a per discharge amount (see Chapter 2), then buying a new MRI to be used only on inpatients may generate a lot of new gross charges, but no additional cash.

13. **Will granting your request generate more operating expenses?** If so, how much and when will they begin? Most requests do seem to generate expenses. Again, finance can help you with this. One very common scenario might be a piece of capital equipment that will require a maintenance contract. It may be that you acquired the new equipment last year and the warranty will expire this year, so a maintenance contract will need to be purchased.

14. **Will granting your request require the hiring of any new FTEs?** If so, how many and when? Labor management is always a major focus—both during the budget, and during the year. It is because at all hospitals, it is the single largest expense, AND it is an expense that can easily and quickly get out of control if it is not managed tightly. Consequently, at most hospitals, during both the budgeting process and during the year, there will be tight controls on adding new positions.

*Note: **Exhibit 6** shows a sample completed form for a capital item.*

Chances are, if you are required to prepare these forms, this will be one of the first things you do in the budget process. Having these requests allows management to look at all of them before the budgets for the "recurring" business are done to see if adjustments are required. For example, if you requested capital to renovate a Nursing unit, then obviously, if that capital is approved, the Nursing unit will be closed for at least part of the year. If the hospital is very busy, and the unit needing renovations is currently in use, then this closure may affect how much volume can be budgeted.

Some hospitals do not require this process. Personally, I prefer it because it provides an avenue for you to be engaged in the planning and budgeting process, so that during the year, while you are being held accountable for delivering the budgeted results, you feel like you understand what is in the budget.

EXHIBIT 6		
J Lee Community Hospital **Budget Request**	Budget Dept Use Only	Request #_____
	Approved?	Y N

Fiscal Year Ending		2012
Department Name		ED
Name of Request		Standardize Defibrillators throughout hospital

Total Money Requested:		
Operating Funds		$ 0
Capital Funds (quote must be attached)		$ 150,000

Capital Requests only:		
Fiscal quarter funds are needed (circle one)		① 2 3 4
Priority rating (A = Mandatory, B = Urgent, C = Needed but not urgent)		A B Ⓒ

Is this request associated with compliance with a new regulatory requirement?		Y Ⓝ
Is this request associated with compliance with an existing but deficient regulatory requirement?		Y Ⓝ
If you answered Yes to either question, please reference the code at issue.		

Describe your request:		
Replace old, mixed defibrillator models with 15 new, standard models		

Describe the benefits to the hospital of granting your request		
Having 1 standard model of defibrillator throughout the hospital will provide a safer environment for patients.		

Describe the risks to the hospital if your request is not granted		
Having old and more importantly mixed models of defibrillators throughout the hospital poses risks to patients.		

Will granting your request increase Net Revenues?		Y Ⓝ
If so, how much per month (detail needs to be attached)?		$
If so, what month will revenues begin?		J F M A M J J A S O N D

Will granting your request increase expenses?		Y Ⓝ
If so, how much per month (detail needs to be attached)?		$
If so, what month will expenses begin?		J F M A M J J A S O N D

Will granting your request require additional FTEs to be hired?		Y Ⓝ
If so, how many?		
If so, what month will the increase begin?		J F M A M J J A S O N D

Does this request have IT implications (hardware/software/interfaces/training)?		Y Ⓝ

Prepared by (printed name)	Thomas Sattler	
Submitted by (Director Signature)	*Thomas Sattler*	
Date submitted	3/25/1974	

Chapter 6 Self Review Questions

1. You are the Director for the department of Pharmacy.

   a. Budget preparation is beginning for FY2012.

   b. Your hospital requires strategic initiative requests be prepared for both operating and capital requests.

   c. You would like the hospital to add automated drug dispensing equipment to the Emergency Department.

   d. Research shows this equipment will improve dispensing and charge capture.

   e. It will also reduce staffing costs by one (1) FTE. This FTE earns $75,000 a year, plus benefits which run approximately 20% of salary costs.

   f. The equipment can be purchased for $100,000.

   g. In addition, the IT Department will need to write an interface. IT has given you an estimate of $5,000 to build and test the interface.

   h. You would like to acquire the equipment in the second quarter.

   i. You consider this request urgent.

   j. The request is not associated with any regulatory requirements.

Using the blank form, shown in **Exhibit 5**, complete a Strategic Initiative Request Form for the request.

CHAPTER 7

Budgeting Statistics and Revenue

In this chapter, we will take a look at budgeting statistics and revenues. We'll start with statistics. All hospital departments are typically assigned a statistic. Once the statistics budgets are set, they are used during budget preparation to compute *things that change when volume changes*—things such as revenue, and sometimes labor and/or supplies. If your department does not generate revenue, you may or may not still generate your own statistic.

Do you know what your department statistic is? Some examples are:

- Med/Surg Nursing units - equivalent patient days (includes inpatient days and observation patients)

- Labor and Delivery units - number of deliveries

- MRI - scans performed

- Pharmacy - doses or orders

- Admitting - registrations

- Surgery - surgery minutes or surgery cases

- Dietary - meals served (including both patient and guest meals in the cafeteria)

If a department does not generate a statistic based upon function, it will typically be assigned one. For example, hospital Administration's statistic is usually adjusted patient days. Human Resource's is hospital FTEs. Housekeeping is usually related to the square footage of the hospital building(s). So a Statistic is the measurement most closely relevant to the resources used to do the tasks carried out by that department. Think about that for a minute—

". . . the measure most closely relevant to the resources used to do the tasks carried out by that department . . ."

Now look again at the examples above, starting with the Med/Surg Nursing unit, all the way down to housekeeping. In each department, you can easily see that the larger their statistic, the more resources they will need to do their jobs.

A larger Nursing unit (higher census) will require more nurses.

The more meals Dietary serves, the more staff they will need to prepare and deliver them.

The larger the hospital (the more APDs they have), the larger the Administration department needs to be to handle daily complexities.

The more employees there are, the more staff will be required in HR to manage their benefits, hiring, orientation paperwork, etc.

Why do all departments require a statistic? Having a statistic associated with the department allows for metrics—such as revenue per patient day in a Nursing unit—or for salary cost per meal served and food cost per meal served in Dietary. Those metrics can then be used to prepare the budgeted revenues, salaries and supplies. They can also be used to compare one hospital to another. When trying to determine whether hospital salaries may be too high, it is useful to be able to compare, for example, salary cost per lab test between one hospital and those of other hospitals in the area or across the country.

Budgeting statistics is perhaps the single most important element of the budget process. In most cases, over 75% of the dollars associated with the budget are calculated using the statistics. In fact, the statistics *drive* the budget! They drive 100% of the operating revenues, and well over 50% of the expenses.

Once again, there is a chance that you will either not participate in the process at all or will simply review work done by others as it affects your department, but a basic understanding of the over-all process will help you put other things in context and see the whole picture more clearly. And when you are comparing actual results against the budget during the year, it may also be useful to understand how your department's budget was built. So for purposes of this chapter, I will assume that you do participate in setting statistic budgets for at least your department. Also, if you sit on a Budget Committee you may actually have the opportunity to participate in the setting of the global budget assumptions for your hospital, so hopefully this chapter will help arm you to participate if given the chance.

STEP 1: HOSPITAL DISCHARGES

Interestingly, at the very core of the budget is a statistic that is not assigned to any department: it is the number of patients you expect to come through your doors for care. You start there, and then answer the question, "What services will they need?" The answers you come up with will set the statistics for most departments in any hospital.

So let's start with *inpatient volumes*. The first statistic to be budgeted is hospital discharges. Discharges may come through your "back door"—as inpatient admissions that came through your emergency room. Or they may come through your "front door"—as a physician referral (e.g., during a patient's annual physical, the doctor determines a need for surgery. He schedules it with the hospital for a specific day in the future, and on that day, the patient arrives at the hospital for the procedure). Emergency room patients may either bring themselves, or be brought by ambulance.

Depending on the level of sophistication of your hospital's budget process, the discharge budget may be developed for each of these categories and added together, or developed as a single total. Either way, the number of discharges budgeted for next year is typically set using the following formula:

Last year's volume
minus
discontinued or closed services
plus
expected growth
equals
next year's volume

The formula may be applied to the hospital as a whole, or it may be broken down by department, or it may be based on the type of service provided (such as general surgery vs. medicine vs. orthopedic surgery vs. OB patients), and summed to arrive at totals for the hospital as a whole. However it is done, the approach is basically the same.

STEP 2: AVERAGE LENGTH OF STAY (ALOS)

Once discharges for the entire hospital have been set, assumptions need to be made for how long (on average) each patient will stay. In this situation, a similar approach is used as in developing the budget for discharges:

Last year's average length of stay (ALOS)
plus or minus
any anticipated or planned changes
equals
next year's ALOS

Anticipated changes may include budgeted initiatives to eliminate discharge delays that will get patients home faster (thereby reducing the length of stay). This process may be very simple—last year's number may be used, or it may be very sophisticated—looking at what services the "new" patients will receive and whether these patients will stay longer (i.e., they are sicker), or shorter (i.e., you plan to grow OB services, which typically have a short stay). You will probably not be directly involved in this portion of the budget, but you should know that this step exists and have a basic understanding of how it is handled by the financial people.

STEP 3: INPATIENT DAYS

Now that the budgets have been set for Discharges and ALOS, we can compute inpatient days:

Discharges *multiplied* **by**
Average Length of Stay *equals*
Inpatient Days

STEP 4: OBSERVATION

As previously noted in Chapter 2, Observation patients are handled just like an inpatient in terms of being in a bed and receiving care, lab tests, meals, etc., but because of reimbursement rules they are not counted in the inpatient numbers. So they need to be added. And we return (once again) to our tried and true approach to budgeting them, as follows:

Last year's volume *plus or minus*
planned changes *equals*
next year's volume

Note: If your hospital has received a lot of denials (see Chapter 2) for unnecessary admissions, there may need to be a plan for more closely scrutinizing admissions criteria before patients are admitted. This may reduce inpatient admissions, but such a policy will inevitably increase the number of observation cases.

Once the number of Observation cases is budgeted, you may need to take one more step to translate those cases into equivalent days. This is similar to translating inpatient discharges into patient days by multiplying by ALOS.

So to calculate Equivalent Observation Days, use the following formula:

Observation cases
multiplied by
average number of observations hours per case
equals
Observation hours.
Then,
Observation hours
divided by
24
equals
Equivalent Observation days

STEP 5: AVERAGE DAILY CENSUS (ADC)

As you read in Chapter 1, ADC stands for Average Daily Census. And this number may either include or exclude Observation patients, depending on hospital policy.

I am a purist on this question, and prefer to exclude Observation patients. So in this book, we will exclude them. (I'm the author, so I'm allowed, right?)

To arrive at the ADC number, the formula looks like this:

Budgeted inpatient hospital days
divided by
the number of calendar days (in month or the year)
equals
budgeted ADC.

This calculation may be done for each Nursing unit—then rolled up to obtain the hospital's total budgeted census, or they may be done in the opposite direction—for the entire hospital, then allocated back to the individual Nursing units.

Note: Nursing units are really the only departments that need to have a computed ADC budget. They will add up their unit's inpatient ADC and Observation ADC, using the total as the basis upon which to budget labor. All other departments will simply use their applicable Statistic for the entire month.

STEP 6: ANCILLARY SERVICES - INPATIENT

Once hospital discharges and inpatient days have been budgeted, the inpatient volumes for the ancillary departments can be derived. An Ancillary department is one that provides services that are *ancillary* to nursing. From a finance perspective, there are three types of departments in a hospital: Nursing, Ancillary Services, and Overhead (also sometimes called Support or Fixed departments).

In Chapter 2 we discussed the hospital's CDM. The "catalog" that lists every service a hospital offers, and the price of that service. In a perfect world, I suppose a budget would be prepared for each and every item in the CDM. Perhaps someday technology will make that possible. For now, for budgeting purposes, we only budget for 1 statistic in each department. It is usually the sum of all procedures performed. For example, there are 1,000's of drugs dispensed in a pharmacy. There is not a volume budgeted for each drug. There is simply a volume budgeted for total doses dispensed. So how is that volume budgeted?

The simple approach to this is to apply a predetermined ratio to the hospital discharges budget. This ratio, which serves to indicate the average utilization of the department for each hospital discharge, will vary for each department. For example, historical information will be used to calculate, on average, how many lab tests are performed on each inpatient discharge. The formula to use here is:

Total inpatient lab tests performed *divided by*
total hospital discharges *equals*
average number of tests per discharge.

For example, if there were 1,000 lab tests performed on a total of 100 discharges, then on average, there were 10 tests performed per discharge. So if next year's budget is going to be 200 discharges, then the formula to calculated the number of lab tests to budget is:

200 discharges x 10 average tests per discharge = 2,000 lab tests to budget.

This formula assumes nothing is planned to change. What if management plans to educate physicians better so that fewer tests are ordered? If successful, then the average number of tests per discharge will drop from 10 to something less. The same process is applied to most ancillary departments that generate inpatient volume (revenue).

STEP 7: OTHER "INDEPENDENT" INPATIENT DEPARTMENT STATISTICS

Some departmental Statistics are budgeted independent of discharges. Surgery, Cath Lab and Deliveries are three common examples. Although they *could* be prepared using the overall ratios as in Step 6, (i.e. a ratio of average number of surgeries per discharge), a more direct approach is usually taken for these departments. These departmental budgets are prepared in a fashion similar to the approach used for hospital discharges:

Last year's volume *minus*
discontinued services *plus*
expected growth *equals*
next year's volume.

STEP 8: OUTPATIENT VOLUME STATISTICS

Unlike inpatient department statistic budgets, which are primarily driven from inpatient discharges, outpatient volume statistics usually each stand independent of one another. Budgeting this volume is fairly straightforward and is simply done one department at a time. As always, we apply our (now well-known) basic formula:

Last year's volume *minus*
discontinued services *plus*
expected growth *equals*
next year's volume

Discontinued services might include the shutting down of a service that had very low volumes, such as diabetes testing. Or management may have initiatives to reduce the number of CTs ordered, which would reduce volume in the CT department.

Examples

Let's walk through a few examples at the department level to demonstrate how you would want to approach this if given the task.

Example 1: Surgery (Perioperative) Services

Let's say you are the Director in charge of the hospital's Perioperative Services and have been tasked with preparing the volume budget for your departments. Your departments probably include (at the very least) the Operating rooms (surgery), pre-op, post-op, and anesthesia. Where to start? In this example, all your department's volumes are dependent on the volume associated with one department—Surgery. There is no pre-op, post-op or anesthesia without surgery. So if you can figure out surgery, you can figure out the rest. Does that seem a little simpler now? Not really hard when you just think for a minute, is it?

Now, where do you start to figure out surgery volumes? Remember the simple formula:

> **Last year's volume *minus*
> discontinued or closed services *plus*
> expected growth *equals*
> next year's volume**

Start by obtaining a report of surgery volume for each of the past 12-months. That will give you last year's volume. Next, meet with administration and business development. If there are business development initiatives going on that are expected to affect your department, they will fill you in.

In your position, you probably already know much of what is already going on in your department, but they can fill you in on anything you don't know about activities and planned activities for growing volumes.

There may be new physicians coming to the hospital. If so, when? What types of cases will they bring? How many cases?

Or there may be physicians retiring (which would come under discontinued services). Maybe a physician left last month, so all the business she brought this past year will not repeat next year. Other issues may need to be discussed. For example, are you operating at capacity with long wait times to schedule? If so, perhaps there is a plan to find ways to improve throughput that would allow more surgery to be scheduled?

All kinds of different things could be going on. And more than one meeting may well be needed to settle on what changes in volume you need to budget. But when you have all the information you need, you can sit down and prepare your own simple "walkforward" of surgery cases. You will need to do two; one for *inpatient cases,* and another for *outpatient cases.* The reason you need to do them separately is that you will need to budget the revenue separately. **Exhibit 7** *(next page)* shows a simple example of a walkforward. As you can see, it is very straightforward.

	Oct.	Nov.	Dec.	Jan.	Feb.	Mar.	Apr.	May	Jun.	Jul.	Aug.	Sep.	Total
EXHIBIT 7													
J Lee Community Hospital													
FYXXX Budget													
Surgery Volume Walkforward													
Current Year Cases	802	758	923	650	618	822	779	890	812	878	956	835	9,723
Volume to be added:													
New OR opening	-	-	-	-	-	40	50	60	70	80	80	80	460
New surgeons		10	10	10	10	10	10	10	10	10	10	10	110
Volume eliminated:													
Surgeon A retiring	(22)	(25)	(19)	(14)	(20)	(10)	(26)	(23)	(22)	(30)	(8)	(19)	(238)
Surgery Cases FYXX	780	743	914	646	608	862	813	937	870	938	1,038	906	10,055
Average minutes per case	85	85	85	85	85	85	85	85	85	85	85	85	85
Surgery minutes FYXXX	66,300	63,155	77,690	54,910	51,680	73,270	69,105	79,645	73,950	79,730	88,230	77,010	854,675

Now that you have surgery volumes budgeted, you can prepare the volume budgets for your other departments relatively simply. Apply what you know (or data you can gather) to do this: the number of pre-op patients and the number of post-op patients should be the same as the number of surgery patients, right (unless your department also recovers patients from other procedure areas like Cath lab)? Voila! You're done.

Example 2: Admitting

Admitting is an example of a department that does not generate revenue but does generate it's own statistic: **registrations**. Registrations are different from the number of admissions because there are many patients who come to the hospital for services but are not admitted. Think of all the patients who come for lab work, imaging services, outpatient surgery, and the largest—emergency room. Every single patient must be registered.

Registration volumes may be budgeted multiple ways. The simplest (if you are the Director in charge) is to require each department that provides services to patients you register prepare their budgets first. Then simply gather their data and add it all together. In actual practice, your hospital's computerized budget system may do that for you.

Example 3: Housekeeping (EVS)

Remember the purpose of a statistic. It is to be able to budget revenues and/ or expenses, then have a metric to monitor against. Housekeeping does not generate a statistic, but we want it to have one. Most hospitals use the dimensions of the hospital building (in square feet). That allows budgeting and monitoring things like the cost of cleaning supplies on a per square foot basis. The cost of labor can also be calculated on a per square foot basis. The good news is that unless there is an expansion in progress, if you are in charge of this department, your statistic is the same every year. Aren't you lucky that way?

Example 4: Pharmacy

Pharmacy is a department whose inpatient volume is a function of hospital discharges.

To set the inpatient volume statistic, look at your current year data. *Simply divide the total doses issued by the number of hospital discharges over the period.*

Let's say that number is 50. That means that you have calculated, on average, that each patient admitted to the hospital receives 50 doses of drugs. So if the budget calls for 2,000 discharges in the month of January, then the pharmacy should budget 2,000 x 50 = 100,000 doses.

To set your outpatient volume, simply take the current year projected volume and add an expected growth percentage, which, as mentioned earlier, is usually assigned by administration.

Your department(s) may be not line up exactly with any of these examples. But the point is the *thought process*. It is the same every time. It may look slightly different from one department to the next, but it is always essentially the same; i.e.,

**Last year's volume plus or *minus*
anticipated changes *equals*
next year's volume.**

BUDGETING GROSS REVENUE

Once statistics are budgeted, budgeting Gross Revenue is very simple and straightforward. Remember that we used historical data as a starting point to budget volume statistics? Gross revenue is budgeted in a similar manner. Using historical inpatient gross revenues and historical inpatient volume statistics, an Average Gross Revenue per statistic is computed. For example, if the pharmacy financial statements for the prior year showed $1,000,000 of Gross inpatient revenue, and 35,000 doses, then the average gross revenue per dose is $1,000,000 / 35,000 = $28.57.

$28.57 is loaded into the budget software as the average revenue per dose. Then, the computer multiplies the $28.57 x the number of inpatient doses budgeted for the coming fiscal year, and bingo! You have your budget for inpatient gross pharmacy revenue. The exact same logic is used to compute the outpatient revenue.

The revenue for each department is computed this way. There are a few added twists: Changes in rates and changes in Payor Mix/Financial Classes.

CHANGES IN RATES

Just like all businesses, hospitals periodically raise their rates. Since we've already discussed in **Chapter 2** that hospitals are almost never paid according to what they charge, you may wonder why they bother. There are actually several reasons. Most are outside the scope of this book. But if you are responsible for setting pricing for new items in your CDM, you may want to be aware of one very important reason that hospitals keep their rates current: Most payors only pay the *lesser of* the fee schedule amount or the hospital's gross charge. "What?" you say. Let me illustrate. Remember from **Chapter 2** that outpatient services are paid on a fee schedule. That is, the payor has a schedule showing what it will pay the hospital for each procedure. Let's use a simple X-ray as an example. If the payor's fee schedule calls for a payment of the lesser of the hospital charge or $10, then if the hospital charge is $8, the payor will only pay $8, but if the hospital charge for the same X-ray was $12, the payor would pay $10. Imagine if a hospital never raised their rates. Eventually, their costs would exceed what their charges were, and payors would therefore be paying them less than their cost. So it is important for hospital's to always make sure their charges are greater than their costs. Rate increases may be done anytime, but are frequently done in conjunction with the budget and take effect with a new fiscal year. Sometimes rates are raised "across the board" for all services, and sometimes increases are specific to certain services. If your department is going to have a rate increase, you have probably been involved in the decision. For illustration purposes, let's say that the decision was made to raise rates in your department by 5%. The 5% would simply be added to the average rate when the budget is loaded into the computer. Pretty simple.

CHANGES IN PAYOR MIX/FINANCIAL CLASSES

As discussed in **Chapter 1**, Payor Mix refers to the relative percentages of business the hospital has for each of it's payors (e.g. 50% Medicare, 25% Medicaid, and 25% Self-pay patients would be an example of a hospital payor mix). Gross revenue is actually budgeted for each *financial class*. We have not talked about financial classes before. As we discussed in **Chapter 2**, hospitals may have contracts with 100's of different payors. To simplify reporting, payors are grouped into *financial classes* that have similarities. Traditional Medicare is one, Medicaid programs are usually grouped together, Managed Medicare is usually one, uninsured (self-pay) patients are another, and then all the remaining managed care plans may be grouped together as one financial class called Managed Care. So if you were to look at your departmental Trial Balance (see **Chapter 3** if you don't remember what a Trial Balance is), you would see gross revenues for each major financial class. The relative percentages of each major financial class is called your payor mix.

After the total inpatient and outpatient gross revenue has been budgeted for each department, then that revenue needs to be sorted into financial classes. If the hospital is anticipating that the payor mix next year will be the same as it was last year, then it will probably simply apply last year's percentages to next year's revenue. If the budget is based on the payor mix shifting, then adjustments will need to be made.

Setting and applying payor mix to revenues is not something you will be involved in, but it helps to understand it I think.

BUDGETING REVENUE DEDUCTIONS/NET REVENUE

So why does payor mix matter for your department? For day to day purposes, it may not matter. It may be something you rarely look at. For budgeting purposes, it only matters because the hospital needs to know what *total* gross revenues are for each financial class in order to budget revenue deductions and net revenue. Remember revenue deductions? We discussed them in **Chapter 2**. Generally speaking, financial classes usually contain payors who pay the same way (DRG or per diem), so a budget is prepared separately for each financial class. The easiest thing to understand is that revenue deductions aren't really budgeted. Based on the volume statistics and gross revenues, Net Revenues are budgeted. Revenue Deductions are simply the "plug" amount between Gross revenues and net revenues. For example, if gross revenues are budgeted to be $1,000,000, and net revenue is calculated (the sum of the calculated net revenue for each financial class) to be $200,000, then revenue deductions must be $800,000 ($1,000,000 - $200,000 = $800,000). The details of how revenue deductions are budgeted varies greatly by hospital, depending on the sophistication of their computer systems, and sometimes depending on the skill level of the finance staff. The BEST news for you, is to remember that revenue deductions are not budgeted at the department level. For all these reasons then, I have decided to leave the budgeting of them outside the scope of this book.

Don't worry. We will revisit how all this comes together later in the book. For now I just wanted you to have a glimpse of how gross revenues, revenue deductions, and net revenues are budgeted.

So did this chapter seem pretty easy? And you thought budgeting was going to be hard! Stay tuned!

Chapter 7 Self Review Questions

1. What is the goal when setting a statistic for a department?

2. Why is budgeting statistics the single most important element of the budget process?

3. What is the general formula for budgeting volume?

4. If ADC for the year is budgeted to be 300, and ALOS is budgeted at 3.3 days, how many discharges are being budgeted?

5. If lab volumes this year averaged 10 tests per adjusted discharge, and next year's budget calls for 10,000 discharges, an adjustment factor of 1.75, and a reduction in utilization of 5%, how many lab tests should be budgeted for next year?

Budgeting Labor

Budgeting *labor* may be the most complex part of preparing a budget for some departments, and the simplest part for others. When you look at the budget for the entire hospital, you will see that labor (including salaries, contract labor, and employee benefits) probably totals more than 50% of the entire operating expense budget. Accurately budgeting, and tightly managing labor can be the difference between a hospital's making a healthy margin and going broke.

Hospital labor is divided into two types: **Fixed and Variable.**

Fixed labor refers to the dollars associated with staff who work the same number of hours, regardless of the census in the hospital. The hospital CEO (Chief Executive Officer) is an example of Fixed labor, while a nurse in a Nursing unit is an example of Variable labor, since the CEO's schedule does not increase or decrease when hospital volumes increase or decrease, whereas the nurse's schedule is tied directly to the volumes of the Nursing unit. If volume goes down, s/he may experience shift shortening—or even shift cancellation. On the other hand, if volumes go up, additional staff may need to be brought in, or overtime may be required.

No department operates with completely variable labor, and no department operates with completely fixed labor. Within a relevant range, most departments require some fixed level of staffing, and even departments that are considered to run with 100% fixed staffing will have fewer FTEs in a smaller hospital than in a larger hospital. For example, in a hospital with an average census of 30, the department of Administration will likely have significantly fewer FTEs than the same department in a hospital with an average census of 500.

Ancillary departments are similarly affected. In a lab, for example, if the department is highly automated, the number of tests that may be performed with a small number of staff is very high. But at the same time, that same number of staff is required even if volumes drop dramatically.

In a Nursing unit, staffing is normally based on a staffing matrix. Staff is added or taken away at step intervals, based on company, industry, or—in some states—legally required ratios.

An example matrix is shown in **Exhibit 8**.

Although the staffing may be considered variable because it moves when volume changes, within a pre-established range of need, the actual staffing may remain unchanged even when volume changes. For example, using the matrix in **Exhibit 8**, when census was between 26 and 30, the staffing stayed the same (was fixed).

Of course, over-all hospital patient volumes do not stay static over the course of any given eight- or twelve-hour shift that someone will be scheduled

EXHIBIT 8										
J Lee Community Hospital										
Nursing Matrix - Medical Unit										
Fiscal Year Ending September 30, 2010										
A	**B**	**C**	**D**	**E**	**F**	**G**	**H**	**I**	**J**	**K**
	7a - 7p					*7p - 7a*				
Census	Director	Charge	Sec'y	PCA	RN	Director	Charge	Sec'y	PCA	RN
50	1	2	3	5	10	0	1	2	4	10
49	1	2	3	5	10	0	1	2	4	10
48	1	2	3	5	10	0	1	2	4	10
47	1	2	3	5	10	0	1	2	4	10
46	1	2	3	5	10	0	1	2	3	10
45	1	2	2	5	9	0	1	2	3	9
44	1	2	2	4	9	0	1	2	3	9
43	1	2	2	4	9	0	1	2	3	9
42	1	2	2	4	9	0	1	2	3	9
41	1	2	2	4	9	0	1	2	3	9
40	1	2	2	4	8	0	1	1	3	8
39	1	2	2	4	8	0	1	1	3	8
38	1	2	2	4	8	0	1	1	3	8
37	1	2	2	4	8	0	1	1	3	8
36	1	2	2	4	8	0	1	1	3	8
35	1	2	2	4	7	0	1	1	3	7
34	1	2	2	3	7	0	1	1	3	7
33	1	2	2	3	7	0	1	1	3	7
32	1	2	2	3	7	0	1	1	3	7
31	1	2	2	3	7	0	1	1	3	7
30	1	1	2	3	6	0	1	1	2	6
29	1	1	2	3	6	0	1	1	2	6
28	1	1	2	3	6	0	1	1	2	6
27	1	1	2	3	6	0	1	1	2	6
26	1	1	2	3	6	0	1	1	2	6
25	1	1	2	3	5	0	1	1	2	5

to work. In some cases, staff schedules may be changed at the last minute, either by adding overtime or by cutting shifts short. But if a hospital does that too often, employees may seek other jobs with more stable and predictable hours (and pay). A balance must be maintained.

All of these factors make preparing a good labor budget very complex.

The scope of this chapter will be to demonstrate preparation of *four types of budgets:*

- a 100% variable budget (such as Surgery),
- a 100% fixed budget (such as Medical Records),
- a combination semi-variable and semi-fixed budget (such as Lab)
- a Nursing unit

As previously mentioned, all departments routinely use a combination of variable and fixed hours to accommodate staffing needs. Nursing departments generally make up one third to one half of a hospital's total labor budget, which means that accuracy is more important in these departments, so they typically require a more sophisticated budget preparation. Other departments have relatively straightforward budget approaches.

Let's look at each budgeting "type." We'll start with the easiest—100% Variable budgets.

100% VARIABLE STAFFING BUDGETS

Usually when a department budget is prepared as 100% variable, it is because staffing is too complicated and typically will change radically as volume changes.

Surgery is one example.

To prepare a 100% variable budget, follow these steps:

1. Determine overall hospital volumes (discharges, surgeries, deliveries, etc.)

2. Based on overall hospital volumes, determine the volumes for the department (i.e., determine the department statistic). A statistic for each month is required.

3. Agree on a man hour per stat number to be budgeted. Two statistics will actually be required:

    a. worked Man Hours/stat, and

    b. the add-on for non-productive time (such as Earned Time Off (ETO)) to compute a paid MH/stat. These stats may be based on department history, or on a company or industry standard.

4. Agree on an average hourly rate (AHR) to be used. A rate for each month will be needed. Typically, the department's current blended rate is used, and it is increased if and when a merit raise is planned.

Voila! For each month, the department's labor budget is a simple formula:

Department statistic *times*
worked MH/stat *times*
(1 + non-productive %) *times*
AHR *equals*
Department labor budget

Let's demonstrate this with an example for a Surgery department:

1. Budgeted surgeries for January: 900

2. Budgeted average minutes per surgery: 85

3. Budgeted surgery statistic (minutes) is then: 900 surgeries times 85 minutes each equals 76,500 minutes of surgery

4. Budgeted worked MH/stat is to be set at: .11 (.11 worked hours of labor per minute of surgery performed)

5. Budgeted non-productive %: 10%

6. Budgeted Paid MH/stat is then: .11 x (1 + 10%) = .121 paid hours of labor per surgery minute

7. Budgeted paid hours of labor for January are then: .121 paid hours per minute x 76,500 minutes = 9,256.50 hours

8. Budget average hourly rate (AHR): $32.50

9. Salary budget for January is then: 9,256.50 hours x $32.50 per hour = $300,836.30

10. FTE budget for January is 9,256.50 hours / # hours per FTE = 9,256.50 / 176 = 52.40

The advantages of this budget model is that it is simple; the disadvantage is that it is not very precise.

FIXED STAFFING BUDGETS

Fixed staffing budgets are also relatively simple to prepare. Once hospital volume budgets have been completed, the number and skill levels of staff required are determined.

In it's simplest form, a small, fixed department labor budget having three FTEs making an AHR of $20/hr looks like this:

3 staff *times*
2080 hours each *times*
an overall average hourly rate of $20/hour *equals*
$124,800 per year *divided by*
12 *equals*
$10,400 per month

The drawbacks to this approach are:

- it may not accurately represent the correct skill mix and average hourly rate

- it does not consider that months with 31 days will have a higher cost than months with 30 (or 28) days.

- it does not reflect any merit increases.

A more detailed approach is illustrated in **Exhibit 9** *(next page)*. Here, the department leader (or designee) populates a typical weekly schedule of staffing needs based on the volumes being budgeted, along with each person's actual rate of pay. This approach assumes that volumes throughout the year will stay within the relevant range, and, the staffing levels required will not vary. In this example, the department is open around the clock, Monday through Friday, with one person working, and open 8 a.m. to midnight on Saturday and Sunday, with one person working.

The steps to completing this budget are:

1. Determine the hospital volumes to be budgeted.

2. Based on hospital volumes, determine the volumes for the department.

3. Based on budgeted volumes for the department, determine appropriate staffing schedules to provide desired coverage.

4. Obtain the pay rates for each person in the department, and if needed, for proposed added staff.

5. Prepare a staffing schedule, and populate each person's pay rate. This step is illustrated in *columns A through J* of **Exhibit 9**.

6. Based on each person's proposed hours to be worked, and their hourly pay rate, calculate salary expense for each person for each month. The model shown in **Exhibit 9** does it for you, using formulas in columns M through X.

7. Adjust as needed to reflect a merit adjustment during the year. **Exhibit 9** shows it being added in July. Notice the salaries in July are 3% larger than June?

8. Sum each month's total cost *(shown in column Y)*.

9. Determine the percentage of non-productive time to budget (ETO etc). **Exhibit 9** uses 10%, shown on *rows 9 and 23*.

10. Add that amount to each month's budget.

Looking at the top of **Exhibit 9**, you can see how the weekly schedule is translated into the number of hours per month for each staff member.

EXHIBIT 9

Row/Col	A	B	C	D	E	F	G	H	I	J	K	L	M	N	O	P	Q	R	S	T	U	V	W	X	Y
1	HOURS										Days in the month		31 January	28 February	31 March	30 April	31 May	30 June	31 July	31 August	30 September	31 October	30 November	31 December	365 Total
2	Name	Rate/Hr	S	M	T	W	Th	F	S	Total			January	February	March	April	May	June	July	August	September	October	November	December	Total
3	Susie S	$30.00		8	8	8	8	8		40			177	160	177	171	177	171	177	177	171	177	171	177	2,086
4	Tom J	$22.10		8	8	8	8	8		40			177	160	177	171	177	171	177	177	171	177	171	177	2,086
5	Alan R	$22.62	8	8	8	8			8	40			177	160	177	171	177	171	177	177	171	177	171	177	2,086
6	Mary D	$25.03	8				8	8	8	32			142	128	142	137	142	137	142	142	137	142	137	142	1,669
7	Add other staff here												-	-	-	-	-	-	-	-	-	-	-	-	-
8	Total Worked Hours		16	24	24	24	24	24	16	152			673	608	673	651	673	651	673	673	651	673	651	673	7,926
9	Non-Productive %												10.0%	10.0%	10.0%	10.0%	10.0%	10.0%	10.0%	10.0%	10.0%	10.0%	10.0%	10.0%	10.0%
10	Total Paid Hours												740	669	740	717	740	717	740	740	717	740	717	740	8,718
11	Worked FTEs												3.80	3.80	3.80	3.80	3.80	3.80	3.80	3.80	3.80	3.80	3.80	3.80	3.80
12	Paid FTEs												4.18	4.18	4.18	4.18	4.18	4.18	4.18	4.18	4.18	4.18	4.18	4.18	4.18
13																									
14																		Merit	3.00%						
15	DOLLARS										Days in the month		31 January	28 February	31 March	30 April	31 May	30 June	31 July	31 August	30 September	31 October	30 November	31 December	
16	Name	Rate/Hr									Weekly cost	Divided by 7	January	February	March	April	May	June	July	August	September	October	November	December	Total
17	Susie S	$30.00									$1,200	$171	$5,314	$4,800	$5,314	$5,143	$5,314	$5,143	$5,474	$5,474	$5,297	$5,474	$5,297	$5,474	$63,518
18	Tom J	$22.10									$884	$126	$3,915	$3,536	$3,915	$3,789	$3,915	$3,789	$4,032	$4,032	$3,902	$4,032	$3,902	$4,032	$46,791
19	Alan R	$22.62									$905	$129	$4,007	$3,619	$4,007	$3,878	$4,007	$3,878	$4,127	$4,127	$3,994	$4,127	$3,994	$4,127	$47,892
20	Mary D	$25.03									$801	$114	$3,547	$3,204	$3,547	$3,433	$3,547	$3,433	$3,654	$3,654	$3,536	$3,654	$3,536	$3,654	$42,396
21	Added Staff here										$-	$-	$-	$-	$-	$-	$-	$-	$-	$-	$-	$-	$-	$-	$-
22	Total										$3,790	$541	$16,783	$15,159	$16,783	$16,242	$16,783	$16,242	$17,287	$17,287	$16,729	$17,287	$16,729	$17,287	$200,597
23	Non-Productive %												10.0%	10.0%	10.0%	10.0%	10.0%	10.0%	10.0%	10.0%	10.0%	10.0%	10.0%	10.0%	10.0%
24	Total												$18,462	$16,675	$18,462	$17,866	$18,462	$17,866	$19,015	$19,015	$18,402	$19,015	$18,402	$19,015	$220,657

- At the bottom of the "Hours" section, you see "Total Worked Hours" *(row 8)*

- Next, 10% is added to budget for non-productive time *(row 9)*

- The "Total Paid Hours" is the sum of worked + 10% non-productive time *(row 10)*

- "Worked FTEs" *(row 11)* is computed based on the "Total Worked Hours," and

- "Paid FTEs" *(row 12)* is computed based on the "Total Paid Hours"

The bottom of **Exhibit 9** translates the hours into salary costs based on each person's hourly rate. Again, there is a total for *"Worked"* and a separate total for *"Paid."*

Chances are, if your department budget is prepared using this approach, you will be given a template, and all you will need to do is to populate the names, their schedules, and their current pay rate (which your HR department will provide you). So you can relax! You needn't be an Excel wizard, nor will you need to figure out how all these formulas work. Again, you just need to know your business—how you staff you department and how much you pay your staff. The budget is nothing more than a translation of that information into numbers.

Careful, now. I think you're learning finance-ese! But here come some of the complications, so don't get too complacent.

Even in this simple, small department, the actual labor dollars incurred during the year will vary from the budget. Some of the reasons are:

1. Vacancies and time off by some staff may require other staff to work overtime, which has a higher rate of pay.

2. As turnover occurs, new staff will be hired at different pay rates.

3. If actual volumes differ substantially from the budgeted volumes, staffing adjustments may be made.

We will discuss these issues in more detail in **Chapter 13**.

SEMI-VARIABLE AND SEMI-FIXED BUDGETS

A semi-variable and semi-fixed budget combines the 100% variable and 100% fixed budgeting models. All the steps of each approach are followed, and the results are combined. This approach works well for departments that have fixed minimum staffing around the clock, but then flex staffing up or down according to volume. A lab, imaging center or pharmacy are examples where this approach may be used.

NURSING BUDGETS

Budgeting labor for a Nursing unit may be done by some hospitals using one of the approaches above. If the Nursing unit runs at full capacity most days, so that census is about the same every day (it doesn't matter if it is a large or small unit), then the either the 100% variable approach or the semi-variable approach may be applied. These approaches are relatively simple, and the results will be adequate *when census does not fluctuate very much.*

If census does fluctuate, a more sophisticated approach is preferred. You may be told that your hospital utilizes the 100% variable approach to budget nursing. That may be the case because the only data that the hospital's budgeting software allows to be loaded is the MH/Stat. However, even if that is so, you can still do a better, more comprehensive budget "on the side" to arrive at the appropriate MH/Stat to load for each month, and you can be comfortable that it will provide you adequate resources to hire, train and educate your staff, *and* take good care of your patients.

To do this, you will need:

- a staffing matrix for your unit

- volume budgets for each month including inpatient and observation days

- the AHR for each position in the department (your HR department can give you this)

- a schedule of education requirements for the year. This will vary by department. If you are unsure of how to develop this schedule yourself, you may want to ask for some help from your professional education department

- a working knowledge of Excel, or someone to help you

Once you have all these items, you can put together a great budget! Ready? Let's do it!

Exhibit 8 (Revisted)

Exhibit 8 *(page 70)* showed a sample staffing matrix. Yours may look slightly different, but should contain the same basic information. The column on the left shows potential census levels. If you select a row, and move across the columns, the matrix shows you how the unit is to be staffed. This example is based on a Nursing unit that runs two twelve-hour shifts a day.

If you are not familiar with a nurse staffing matrix, stop here and go take a look and familiarize yourself with it. Think about how your unit has been staffed in the past. How many patients did each nurse take care of? The answer will vary depending on what type of Nursing unit you work in. ICU's run as low as 2:1 (two patients for each nurse), while some low level SNF units may

EXHIBIT 10

J Lee Community Hospital

Nursing Matrix - Medical Unit

Medical Unit

Fiscal Year Ending September 30, 2010

A	B	C	D	E	F	G	H	I	J	K	L	M	N	O	P	Q	R
			7a - 7p				7p - 7a				Total Worked Hours Over a 24 Hour Period						Worked
Census	Director	Charge	Unit secy	PCA	RN	Director	Charge	Unit secy	PCA	RN	Director	Charge	Unit secy	PCA	RN	Total Hrs	MH/Stat
50	1	2	3	5	10	0	1	2	4	10	8	36	60	108	240	452	9.04
49	1	2	3	5	10	0	1	2	4	10	8	36	60	108	240	452	9.22
48	1	2	3	5	10	0	1	2	4	10	8	36	60	108	240	452	9.42
47	1	2	3	5	10	0	1	2	4	10	8	36	60	108	240	452	9.62
46	1	2	3	5	10	0	1	2	3	10	8	36	60	96	240	440	9.57
45	1	2	2	5	9	0	1	2	3	9	8	36	48	96	216	404	8.98
44	1	2	2	4	9	0	1	2	3	9	8	36	48	84	216	392	8.91
43	1	2	2	4	9	0	1	2	3	9	8	36	48	84	216	392	9.12
42	1	2	2	4	9	0	1	2	3	9	8	36	48	84	216	392	9.33
41	1	2	2	4	9	0	1	2	3	9	8	36	48	84	216	392	9.56
40	1	2	2	4	8	0	1	1	3	8	8	36	36	84	192	356	8.90
39	1	2	2	4	8	0	1	1	3	8	8	36	36	84	192	356	9.13
38	1	2	2	4	8	0	1	1	3	8	8	36	36	84	192	356	9.37
37	1	2	2	4	8	0	1	1	3	8	8	36	36	84	192	356	9.62
36	1	2	2	4	8	0	1	1	3	8	8	36	36	84	192	356	9.89
35	1	2	2	4	7	0	1	1	3	7	8	36	36	84	168	332	9.49
34	1	2	2	3	7	0	1	1	3	7	8	36	36	72	168	320	9.41
33	1	2	2	3	7	0	1	1	3	7	8	36	36	72	168	320	9.70
32	1	2	2	3	7	0	1	1	3	7	8	36	36	72	168	320	10.00
31	1	2	2	3	7	0	1	1	3	7	8	36	36	72	168	320	10.32
30	1	1	2	3	6	0	1	1	2	6	8	24	36	60	144	272	9.07
29	1	1	2	3	6	0	1	1	2	6	8	24	36	60	144	272	9.38
28	1	1	2	3	6	0	1	1	2	6	8	24	36	60	144	272	9.71
27	1	1	2	3	6	0	1	1	2	6	8	24	36	60	144	272	10.07
26	1	1	2	3	6	0	1	1	2	6	8	24	36	60	144	272	10.46
25	1	1	2	3	5	0	1	1	2	5	8	24	36	60	120	248	9.92

run as high as 8:1. When you look at this Exhibit, you see that this unit is based on 5:1—rounding up. Notice that every time the census changes by five, another nurse is added. When the census is 25, there are five RNs. When the census is 50, there are 10. The same logic applies to unit secretaries and PCAs, although these positions carry much higher ratios.

Before you continue on, it's important that you are comfortable with this matrix. It is the core of nurse budgeting and productivity.

Are you ready to move to the next step?

Exhibit 10

Exhibit 10 *(page 77)* shows the same staffing matrix as **Exhibit 8** with some columns added on the right for budget-building purposes. Here, total hours are computed for each 24-hour period for each skill level. Hours are computed by multiplying the number of scheduled staff on each shift by the number of hours on the shift. In our example, remember, these are 12-hour shifts. The only exception is the department Director, who is an exempt employee (is paid for 40 hours per week regardless of the number of hours actually worked). This position is therefore shown to work eight hours per day.

Let's stop a minute and look at what we have. Look across the highlighted row. Census is 38.

At a 38 census, over a 24-hour period, the following staff work:

a. One department director works eight hours *(column L)*

b. Two charge nurses each work 12 hours during the day *(column C)*, and one charge nurse works 12 hours at night *(column H)* for a total of 36 hours *(Column M)* over the 24-hour period

c. Two unit secretaries each work 12 hours during the day *(column D)*, and one unit secretary works 12 hours at night *(column I)* for a total of 36 hours *(column N)* over the 24-hour period

d. Four PCAs each work 12 hours during the day *(column E)*, and three PCAs each work 12 hours at night *(column J)* for a total of 84 hours *(column O)* over the 24-hour period

e. Eight RNs each work 12 hours during the day *(column F)*, and another eight RNs work 12 hours each at night *(column K)* for a total of 192 hours *(column P)* over the 24-hour period

f. As shown on the right in the *"Total Hrs" (column Q)*, the sum of items a. through e. above is 356 hours

These 356 hours are the resources to be used to provide care each day when there are 38 patients on the unit.

As shown in *column R*, 356 hours divided by 38 patients equals 9.37 hours worked for each patient. Or, said another way, each patient receives 9.37 hours

EXHIBIT 11

J Lee Community Hospital

Nursing Matrix - Medical Unit

Fiscal Year Ending September 30, 2010

	Total Worked Hours Over a 24 Hour Period					Worked	Average Hourly Rate					Extended Cost						
A	L	M	N	O	P	Q	R	S	T	U	V	W	X	Y	Z	AA	AB	AC	AD
Census	Director	Charge	Unit secy	PCA	RN	Total Hrs	MH/Stat	Director	Charge	Unit secy	PCA	RN	Director	Charge	Unit secy	PCA	RN	Total	Cost per Unit of Service
50	8	36	60	108	240	452	9.04	$50	$40	$15	$15	$35	$400	$1,440	$900	$1,620	$8,400	$12,760	$255
49	8	36	60	108	240	452	9.22	$50	$40	$15	$15	$35	$400	$1,440	$900	$1,620	$8,400	$12,760	$260
48	8	36	60	108	240	452	9.42	$50	$40	$15	$15	$35	$400	$1,440	$900	$1,620	$8,400	$12,760	$266
47	8	36	60	108	240	452	9.62	$50	$40	$15	$15	$35	$400	$1,440	$900	$1,620	$8,400	$12,760	$271
46	8	36	60	96	240	440	9.57	$50	$40	$15	$15	$35	$400	$1,440	$900	$1,440	$8,400	$12,580	$273
45	8	36	48	96	216	404	8.98	$50	$40	$15	$15	$35	$400	$1,440	$720	$1,440	$7,560	$11,560	$257
44	8	36	48	84	216	392	8.91	$50	$40	$15	$15	$35	$400	$1,440	$720	$1,260	$7,560	$11,380	$259
43	8	36	48	84	216	392	9.12	$50	$40	$15	$15	$35	$400	$1,440	$720	$1,260	$7,560	$11,380	$265
42	8	36	48	84	216	392	9.33	$50	$40	$15	$15	$35	$400	$1,440	$720	$1,260	$7,560	$11,380	$271
41	8	36	48	84	216	392	9.56	$50	$40	$15	$15	$35	$400	$1,440	$720	$1,260	$7,560	$11,380	$278
40	8	36	36	84	192	356	8.90	$50	$40	$15	$15	$35	$400	$1,440	$540	$1,260	$6,720	$10,360	$259
39	8	36	36	84	192	356	9.13	$50	$40	$15	$15	$35	$400	$1,440	$540	$1,260	$6,720	$10,360	$266
38	8	36	36	84	192	356	9.37	$50	$40	$15	$15	$35	$400	$1,440	$540	$1,260	$6,720	$10,360	$273
37	8	36	36	84	192	356	9.62	$50	$40	$15	$15	$35	$400	$1,440	$540	$1,260	$6,720	$10,360	$280
36	8	36	36	84	192	356	9.89	$50	$40	$15	$15	$35	$400	$1,440	$540	$1,260	$6,720	$10,360	$288
35	8	36	36	84	168	332	9.49	$50	$40	$15	$15	$35	$400	$1,440	$540	$1,260	$5,880	$9,520	$272
34	8	36	36	72	168	320	9.41	$50	$40	$15	$15	$35	$400	$1,440	$540	$1,080	$5,880	$9,340	$275
33	8	36	36	72	168	320	9.70	$50	$40	$15	$15	$35	$400	$1,440	$540	$1,080	$5,880	$9,340	$283
32	8	36	36	72	168	320	10.00	$50	$40	$15	$15	$35	$400	$1,440	$540	$1,080	$5,880	$9,340	$292
31	8	36	36	72	168	320	10.32	$50	$40	$15	$15	$35	$400	$1,440	$540	$1,080	$5,880	$9,340	$301
30	8	24	36	60	144	272	9.07	$50	$40	$15	$15	$35	$400	$960	$540	$900	$5,040	$7,840	$261
29	8	24	36	60	144	272	9.38	$50	$40	$15	$15	$35	$400	$960	$540	$900	$5,040	$7,840	$270
28	8	24	36	60	144	272	9.71	$50	$40	$15	$15	$35	$400	$960	$540	$900	$5,040	$7,840	$280
27	8	24	36	60	144	272	10.07	$50	$40	$15	$15	$35	$400	$960	$540	$900	$5,040	$7,840	$290
26	8	24	36	60	144	272	10.46	$50	$40	$15	$15	$35	$400	$960	$540	$900	$5,040	$7,840	$302
25	8	24	36	60	120	248	9.92	$50	$40	$15	$15	$35	$400	$960	$540	$900	$4,200	$7,000	$280

of care from the staff on the floor each day. This is called productivity. We will talk more about *productivity* in **Chapter 13**. For now, we just want to focus on how to build a budget.

Exhibit 11

The next piece of the puzzle is to price out the labor costs associated with each census level. **Exhibit 11** *(page 79)* shows our staffing matrix from **Exhibit 8** *(page 70)* and **Exhibit 10** *(page 77)* with yet more columns added *(Columns B through K have been hidden for space purposes)*. These columns show the average hourly rate paid for each skill level. When you prepare your budget, your HR or finance departments can give you this information.

Only two more simple steps remain in our exercise:

1. As shown on **Exhibit 11** *columns X through AB,* simply multiply the rate per hour paid for each skill mix by the number of hours worked to get the extended cost for that skill mix. Then total the sum of all skill mixes to compute the total cost of all the hours worked that day *(column AC)*.

2. The last step is to compute the Cost per Unit of Service. As shown on **Exhibit 11** *column AD,* at a census level of 38, the total cost of care for one day is $10,360 (look across the highlighted row to find this number). This means that when census is 38, it costs $10,360 each day to provide nursing care for these patients, or $273.00 (rounded up to nearest dollar) per patient ($10,360 / 38 = $272.63). We will talk more about Cost per Unit of Service later in this chapter.

Sometimes it takes a few times of going over these concepts to have them all "click." Feel free to go back over this a few times. When you're ready to move on, I'll be right here.

OK, so you're ready to move on? Great! Let's go!

Now you're ready to take a staffing matrix and turn it into a budget. Building on what you've already learned, this will be so simple. You will be amazed how simple it is.

Exhibit 12

Exhibit 12 is a simple budget template. In this illustration, the hospital has a fiscal year that runs from October through September. The budget shown is for fiscal year ending September 30, 2010. Let's start by looking at the budget for October and working our way through it.

- *Row 1* shows the number of days in each month. You'll see how we use that statistic in a moment.

- *Row 2* shows the Average Daily Census (ADC) for that month (see ADC in **Chapter 1** if you don't remember what ADC means). October is budgeted at 38—the same census we used in our earlier examples.

EXHIBIT 12

J Lee Community Hospital
Nursing Budget - Medical Unit
Fiscal Year Ending September 30, 2010

Row		October	November	December	January	February	March	April	May	June	July	August	September	Total
1	Days in Month	31	30	31	31	28	31	30	31	30	31	31	30	365
2	Average Daily Census	38	30	36	38	47	26	29	33	40	50	45	41	38
3	Total Patient Days	1,178	900	1,116	1,178	1,316	806	870	1,023	1,200	1,550	1,395	1,230	13,762
4														
5	Worked MH/Stat	9.37	9.07	9.89	9.37	9.62	10.46	9.38	9.70	8.90	9.04	8.98	9.56	9.40
6	Total Worked Hours	11,036	8,160	11,036	11,036	12,656	8,432	8,160	9,920	10,680	14,012	12,524	11,760	129,412
7	Total Worked Cost/Stat	$272.63	$261.33	$287.78	$272.63	$271.49	$301.54	$270.34	$283.03	$259.00	$255.20	$256.89	$277.56	$271.03
8	Total Worked Cost	$321,160	$235,200	$321,160	$321,160	$357,280	$243,040	$235,200	$289,540	$310,800	$395,560	$358,360	$341,400	$3,729,860
9														
10	Non-Productive %	10%	12%	13%	10%	10%	11%	10%	10%	10%	10%	12%	10%	11%
11	Non-Productive Hours	1,104	979	1,435	1,104	1,266	928	816	992	1,068	1,401	1,503	1,176	13,770
12	Non-Productive Cost	$32,116	$28,224	$41,751	$32,116	$35,728	$26,734	$23,520	$28,954	$31,080	$39,556	$43,003	$34,140	$396,922
13														
14	Total Paid Hours	12,140	9,139	12,471	12,140	13,922	9,360	8,976	10,912	11,748	15,413	14,027	12,936	143,182
15	Total Cost	$353,276	$263,424	$362,911	$353,276	$393,008	$269,774	$258,720	$318,494	$341,880	$435,116	$401,363	$375,540	$4,126,782
16														
17	Paid MH/Stat	10.31	10.15	11.17	10.31	10.58	11.61	10.32	10.67	9.79	9.94	10.06	10.52	10.40
18	Paid $$/UOS	$299.89	$292.69	$325.19	$299.89	$298.64	$334.71	$297.38	$311.33	$284.90	$280.72	$287.72	$305.32	$299.87

Remember this does not mean we are expecting the census to be 38 every day in October—just the overall average over the month. Note: the monthly census would most likely never be budgeted to fluctuate this much in a real hospital. The variations are shown here to illustrate what the impact on cost is when census changes dramatically.

- *Row 3* shows Total Patient Days. Total Patient Days is ADC x number of days in the month. In October, this means that if census averages 38 each day for 31 days, then by the end of the month, there will have been a total of 38 x 31 =1,178 patient days on the unit.

- *Row 5* shows the Worked Man Hours per Stat assigned from the Staffing matrix at the budgeted census level. Remember from our earlier discussion that when census is 38, the total hours of care per patient, per day is 9.37. *(see column R from **Exhibit 10, page 77**).*

- *Row 6* shows Total worked Hours. Since we know that total worked hours per patient day is 9.37 at a census of 38, and if census is 38 for 31 days, then total worked hours over the month will be 9.37 hours per patient day x 1,178 patient days in the month = 9.37 x 1,178 = 11,036 worked hours for the month.

- *Row 7* shows Worked Cost per Stat. Again, as before, when we computed the costs of the director, charge nurse, unit secretary, PCAs, and RNs, in total it came out to $272.63 per patient day when census was 38. Refer back to **Exhibit 11** *(page 79)* column AD if needed.

- *Row 8* shows the computed total worked cost for the month. Using the same logic as *row 6*, if we know that the cost per day at a census of 38 is $272.63, then total worked cost for the month when there are 1,178 patient days must be $272.63 x 1,178 = $321,160.

- *Row 10* is something we haven't talked about yet for nursing budgets: Non-Productive percentage. We keep talking about "worked" hours. Worked hours refers back to the staffing matrix: the hours of time that must be worked to provide the level of care desired, based on the staffing ratios agreed upon by nursing staff and hospital management. However, on any given week, there will be staff unable to work because of illness, vacations, etc. They take time off with pay. In hospitals, this time is usually referred to as ETO (earned time off) or PTO (paid time off). These hours are considered "non-productive." Other examples of non-productive time are hours for bereavement, education, and some hospitals consider orientation time to be non-productive. Whatever it is for, and whatever it is called, it is time that is PAID to employees for hours above and beyond the staffing matrix. It is time that has a cost to it, that needs to be added to the budget for worked hours. For budget purposes, these hours may be computed using sophisticated methods, but usually a historical average percentage is used. The budget shown here uses 10% for most months, with slightly higher percentages for holiday and summer vacation months.

- *Row 11* is computed non-productive time. It is a simple calculation of worked hours from *row 6* x the Non-productive % shown in *row 10*.

- *Row 12* is computed cost of non-productive time. Similar to *row 11*, it is a simple calculation of the worked cost shown on *row 8* x the non-productive % shown on *row 10*.

- *Row 14* shows Total Paid Hours. Total paid hours is the sum of worked hours plus non-productive hours = 11,036 + 1,104 = 12,140 for October.

- *Row 15* shows Total Paid Cost. Total paid cost is the sum of worked cost plus non-productive cost = $321,160 + $32,116 = $353,276 for October.

- *Row 17* shows the Total Paid Hours per Stat. The formula for paid hours per stat is the same as the formula for worked hours per stat, except total paid hours (including both worked and non-productive hours) is used. So for October, the Total Paid Hours per Stat is 12,140 / 1,178 = 10.31. This means that although we only provide 9.37 hours of care to each patient each day, we PAY for a total of 10.31 hours after adding non-productive time.

- *Row 18* shows the Total Cost per Day. Similar to *row 17*: it shows the effect of the added non-productive hours. *Row 18* shows the cost of these hours added to the cost per day of care provided to each patient. *Row 15* showed the total paid cost to be $353,276. *Row 3* shows total patient days for October to be 1,178. Therefore total Paid Cost per Patient Day, including both worked and non-productive time, is $353,276 / 1,178 = $299.89.

Feeling a little overwhelmed, perhaps? Well, the best news is, your hospital probably already has software to do the mathematical calculations for this. All you will need to do is to *understand* how the process works so you can set the assumptions:

- An ADC number that (this time) includes Observation patients

- Agree on the staffing matrix to be employed, and

- Agree on the non-productive time percentage to use.

Everything else will take care of itself.

Some hospitals budget Nursing as a 100% variable department and simply load the same MH/Stat every month. If your hospital is one of these, ask yourself if you census stays about the same every day. If so, then your historical MH/stat can probably be safely used to do next year's budget (unless you want to change your staffing model). If your census fluctuates a lot, or is budgeted to fluctuate a lot next year, then you will want to talk to management.

Go back and look at **Exhibit 10** *(page 77)*. At a census of 26, the department is at it's worst efficiency level, whereas at a census of 40, it is at peak efficiency. As shown on **Exhibit 10** *(page 77)*, at a census of 26, the paid MH/stat is 11.61, but at a census of 40, the paid MH/stat is down to 9.79. The difference between 11.61 MH/stat and 9.79 is significant. We will talk more about that when we discuss productivity in **Chapter 13**.

For now, my point is that you do not want your hospital to budget a straight, across-the-board MH/stat for your department if the budget calls for fluctuating census. If you need to, you can relatively easily build the models shown in this book to at least show them what the MH/Stat needs to be at each budget level. Remember, all of these MH/stat numbers are based on the same staffing matrix. You aren't asking for extra people. You are simply asking for a budget that *reflects* your staffing matrix. And remember,that is what the budget is *supposed* to do—be a numerical presentation of your operating assumptions. So speak up! Don't be shy!

COST PER UNIT OF SERVICE ($$$/UOS)

As we just looked at in the nursing labor budget, the final budget calculation is the Total Cost per Unit of Service ($$$/UOS). But Nursing units aren't the only departments where Cost per UOS are used. All departments use this statistic. When you get everything finished—*this* is the ultimate goal: to figure out how much it will cost you to perform a task in your department each day. For Nursing, it was the Cost per Patient Day. For Lab, it will be the Cost per Test, in Pharmacy it will be the Cost per Dose. Regardless of whether you prepared a budget using fixed FTEs, variable FTEs, or a combination, the Cost per Unit of Service is actually much more important than the hours it takes to do the work. If you could find four people working at $6 per hour who could do the work of one $30 per hour clinical professional, no one would care if you had four FTEs instead of one. In fact, finance would love you—it's cheaper! The problem is, you usually can't. And because you usually can't, the focus will be on the hours side of the equation because the assumption is that controlling the hours is the best way to control the costs.

BUDGETING PREMIUM LABOR COSTS

Premium labor costs are costs incurred that have a "premium" associated with them. If the average hourly rate paid to a nurse in your ICU is $45 per hour, then when you pay that nurse overtime at time-and-a-half, or use registry or agency nurses at $65 per hour, then you are utilizing premium labor.

Unless you have an unlimited labor pool and a beyond-amazing labor management staff, the reality is that you *will* use premium labor sometimes. Should you budget for it? That depends on your institution's viewpoint. Most hospitals will have a goal of *minimizing* the use of premium labor. Some hospitals will budget these costs at zero to "push" this goal. Most hospitals will at least budget a reduction compared to the prior year. Premium labor is expensive, and if it can be managed out of the budget, it can be "easy money" added to your bottom line. Let me demonstrate:

- Let's say an ER normally runs with around 50 paid RN FTEs. Over the course of a 30-day month, one FTE works 171 hours (2,080 hours a year / 365 x 30 days = 171), so 50 FTEs equals 171 x 50 = 8,550 hours.

- If the average rate for an RN is $30, then with no premium labor costs, those 50 RNs would cost 8,550 hours x $30 = $256,500.

- If 10% of those hours were worked as overtime, which pays 150%, then the cost for the hours increase to $269,325, calculated as follows:

8,550 hours x 90% = regular hours = 7,695 x $30/hour = $230,850. Plus 8,550 hours x 10% = overtime hours = 855 x $30 x 150% = $38,475. So the total cost is now $230,850 + $38,475 = $269,325

This represents a "premium" or "extra" cost of $12,825 ($269,325 - $256,500)—a 5% increase in cost—with nothing added to show for it. Think of it this way: that 5% *could* have been used to give a 5% merit raise to everyone in the department instead of paying overtime to just a handful of staff. Or that $12,825 could have paid for 2.5 more RN FTEs in the department, and maybe as many as five additional support staff. *That is why hospitals focus closely on premium labor!*

MERIT AND MARKET ADJUSTMENTS

Hopefully your hospital will be planning to give merit adjustments to their employees at some point during the year. It will be critical to build those increases into the budget. Most budget software has a mechanism to accommodate this easily.

Market adjustments must also be considered. What is a market adjustment? It is an adjustment given to a group of employees doing similar jobs because market conditions require it. Market adjustments can be made for any job category—nurses, lab technicians, administrative assistants, social workers, etc.

Let's use nurses as an example. Because of the nursing shortage that the country has faced for many years, the job market for nurses is very competitive. No nurse ever need worry that s/he cannot find a job. If competitors in your area begin paying a higher wage, your hospital will need to increase their own nurse's wages to avoid losing them to the competition. When the decision is made to do that (in order to be fair) the increase must be given to every nurse. That increase is called a *market adjustment*. Depending on the size of your hospital, and the mix of services you offer, nurses may make up close to half of your work force. Giving half of your workforce a raise of $1 an hour can have an annual cost of millions of dollars. As part of the budget process, the

Human Resources department will usually put forth recommendations based on what they know. How these recommendations are decided on, or loaded into the budget varies widely by hospital. The good news for you is that it is something you needn't worry about in terms of budget preparation. But if no money is budgeted for this, it may be difficult to do. And the cost of not doing it (turnover) can be even more expensive.

BUDGETING BENEFITS

Benefits refers to all those things you sign up for every year: health insurance, dental, flex accounts, as well as benefit costs the hospital pays such as worker's compensation and unemployment insurance, FICA, etc. As you can imagine, the cost associated with these expenses fluctuates based on the number of employees the hospital has (so is not a fixed cost). Most hospitals do not allocate benefit expenses out to the individual departments. It may be a department itself ("the benefit department"), or these costs may be budgeted and charged to the Human Resources department. Other than your fiduciary responsibility as a leader to your hospital as a whole, these are not expenses you will budget or be responsible for monitoring during the year. Managing benefits and modeling potential impacts of changes in benefits can be very complex, and best left to experts (I am not one!). This budget will therefore be prepared by folks that work with benefits every day. So it is beyond the scope of this book.

Whew! You just finished the hardest part of your budget! It's all downhill from here. And if you understand the concepts behind budgeting labor, then you are well on your way to understanding the concepts behind managing it on a daily basis.

Chapter 8 Self Review Questions

1. Name the three approaches to budgeting labor.

2. Compute the annual budget for salaries for the Department of Surgery using the following information: 10,000 surgeries at an average of 65 minutes per surgery. Target productivity for worked hours is .10 hours per minute. Non-productive add-on is 10%. AHR is $30.

3. Using the information from question #2 above, how many worked FTEs need to be budgeted?

4. Using the statistic (minutes) information from #2 above, what is the total cost per UOS (including non-productive time)?

5. If HIM has 10 FTEs and the AHR of the department is $15, and non-productive time is 10%, how much money should be budgeted for the month of February (a 28 day month)?

CHAPTER 9

Budgeting Supplies

Budgeting supply expense is actually quite simple and straightforward. It is certainly much less complicated than budgeting labor! The only thing that makes supply budgeting difficult is that for most hospitals, there are many, many supply accounts in the general ledger that need to be budgeted.

Supplies are grouped in two ways.

The first type of grouping is what is called "Natural Classes." Natural class refers to grouping things that naturally go, well . . . together. Surgical implants, food, forms, uniforms, and drugs would be a few examples. Most hospitals probably have 20-30 natural classes of supplies. If you remember the discussion in **Chapter 3** about sub-accounts in the General ledger (G/L) and on a Trial Balance, then perhaps the easiest way to describe natural classes is that you will see them as the supply expense sub-accounts in the G/L.

The other way to group supplies is by department: Nursing units, surgery, lab, etc. But what actually happens is that each department may use several of the natural classes. So to prepare a budget that has enough detail to allow monitoring and the ability to investigate differences, what you actually need is a budget for *each natural class, each department, and each month!* Imagine even a small hospital with, say, 50 departments. That means that there would be 1,000-1,500 supply accounts. Multiply that by 12-months, and you have over 12,000 numbers to budget, just for supplies! And the number may be ten times that for a larger hospital.

As previously discussed when we were learning about labor, all expenses actually have a fixed component and a variable component. Supplies are no exception. Although the number of bandages that are used, or meals that are served, varies with patient volumes, the number of sticky notes you use probably doesn't have much of a connection. Overall though, supplies probably actually move more consistently with volume than any other expense. For that reason, most hospitals budget supplies as variable, which means supply expense is tied to hospital and/or department volume. Some individual supply accounts may be budgeted strictly as fixed. If you have accounts like that in your department, the approach would be the same approach as we will cover in the next chapter. So I will focus this chapter on budgeting variable supply expenses.

Remember that when we discussed budgeting volume we talked about how even though there are thousands of line items in a CDM, we don't budget for all of them? We simply use a composite statistic that is actually all of the procedures added together? So instead of budgeting 1,000 MRIs with contrast and 200 MRIs without contrast, we simply budget 1,200 MRIs. Budgeting for supply expenses could be approached this way, and in some hospitals it may be. That would make the budget process very simple. But it would be very difficult to investigate variances during the year if your supply spending differs significantly from the budget. You would not have data detailed enough to know where to begin to see where your spending is different than budget. No, we do not prepare a separate budget for every single item you use. We group them into the natural classes discussed above, then do a budget for each natural class and each department.

Another reason you really need to budget separately for each natural class is that one of the keys to preparing an achievable budget is to anticipate inflation where appropriate. Supply inflation varies greatly depending on the type (or natural class) of the items. Drugs and orthopedic implant supplies are two examples where for several years inflation far exceeded inflation of other types of supplies. For example, drug inflation may have run as high as 10-15% for some years, and orthopedic implant inflation has traditionally been 8-10%, while inflation of commodity items (such as gloves and bandages), forms, food, etc may only have been 1-2%. So you would not be able to budget with any level of accuracy unless you budgeted separately for each of these natural classes.

Seem overwhelming? The good news is that, unlike budgeting labor, the *process* for budgeting supplies is the same for every department. That fact alone should make you breathe a sigh of relief! Even more good news is that the folks in finance figure out how to deal with the complexities surrounding how to budget for so many accounts (much of it will be automated).

For purposes of this book, we will simply look at one fictitious department and show how that department's budget would be approached for one month. Let's start by talking about what your role is likely to be. Then we'll talk about how your work will be used to build the budget.

There are four pieces of information that finance needs your help with to build your budget. Look at **Exhibit 13**. This is a spreadsheet that you may be asked to help populate in order to build the budget for your department. It contains the assumptions for your department's supply expenses next year. Going back to the idea about the budget being a one-year slice of a strategic plan, what do you think your story will be next year as it relates to supplies? What is going to *happen?* We need to get those events into the budget. This

		EXHIBIT 13						
		Department Name: Dietary						
Row	Type	Description	Commodities	Food	Implants	Stents	Drugs	Forms
1	Volume	Supply Chain Initiative Natural Class-Specific growth % Adjustment	-10.0%	0.0%	0.0%	0.0%	0.0%	0.0%
2	Volume	Department-Specific initiative growth % adjustment	0.0%	8.0%	0.0%	0.0%	0.0%	-50.0%
3	Price	Natural Class-Specific Expected inflation %	1.5%	3.0%	0.0%	0.0%	0.0%	1.0%
4	Price	Supply chain Pricing-Adjustment initiatives	-4.0%	-2.0%	0.0%	0.0%	0.0%	-25.0%

template provides you the mechanism to tell finance what your events are expected to be as related to supply expense. Let's walk through it together.

First, notice there is a place for the department name at the top. A separate worksheet like this will need to be prepared for each department, as each department will have different answers to populate the cells. Second, notice there is a column for each natural class (for simplicity purposes, I've only shown a few of them). Depending on your department, you will probably not use all of them (for example, dietary does not use implants). OK, let's talk about each of the four rows you need to populate. There are two related to volume, and two related to price:

1. *Supply Chain initiative, natural class–specific, growth % adjustment.* Wow! That's a mouthful, huh? Your hospital may have a shorter name for this. I wanted something that describes for you exactly what it is. Let's break it down. "Supply Chain" is probably a term you know, or have at least heard. It is not specific to health care. Colleges now have it as a major course of study. Supply Chain simply refers to the entire chain of events surrounding supplies. It includes how, what and when to order; how to transport and receive; where to store; how and when to distribute; and finally, how much to pay. Your Purchasing and Materials departments will be in charge of most things "Supply Chain." The numbers that go on this line are usually associated with initiatives that cross departments, but it is important to notice that individual supply chain initiatives are usually targeted at one specific natural class. An example might be that there is a supply chain initiative to reduce waste of commodity goods such as paper towels or gloves. Or to move to only printing forms on demand instead of pre-printing, thereby reducing waste. So each initiative may apply to many departments—but only one natural class. The budget may reflect the same percentage in every department for a given initiative, or some departments may have higher or lower impact percentages depending on the initiative.

2. *Department-specific initiative growth percentage adjustment.* Oh dear. Another mouthful. The percentage you want to input here is one that will adjust growth of supply utilization (in your department) for an initiative that is being incorporated into the budget (see **Chapter 6** for the discussion of budgeting initiatives). Too long of a sentence? Examples always seem to help, I think. Let's say that the hospital was budgeting an initiative to focus on treating HIV patients next year. Although overall hospital volume is budgeted to grow (say) 5%, drug utilization is expected to increase *more* than 5% because of the addition of this drug-intensive service. The percentage you want to input here is the growth *in excess of the overall hospital growth* (that will be already built in —you'll see later). Using our HIV example, let's say overall hospital growth was projected at 5%, but drug growth due to the HIV initiative, was expected to be 8%, then the number to put here is the 3% difference. Make sense?

3. *Natural class-specific expected inflation %.* This is the first of the two price adjusters (the first two rows are volume adjusters). Earlier in this chapter we discussed that the very reason you budget at the natural class level is because inflation will vary. Here is where you account for that. As the leader of your department, you may well be the person best positioned to know what is happening to pricing for supplies that are specific to your department. If you don't know, and are asked what should be put here, you can probably find help online or with your professional associations.

4. *Supply chain pricing adjustment initiatives.* These adjustments will usually be determined by the Supply Chain folks, but you may be involved, depending on the situation. Perhaps the most common of this type of initiative would be where your Supply Chain folks are negotiating with your Purchasing Group (a company that is engaged by multiple hospitals to negotiate pricing) to get better pricing for (say) stents. As you can see, these percentages are specific to each natural class. In our example, I have shown a 4% reduction in commodities, a 2% reduction in food costs, and a 25% reduction in forms expense. These would be 3 different initiatives: the commodities may be tied to changing to a new vendor, food may be re-negotiating with existing vendors, and forms may be a move to bring printing in-house.

Hopefully all of that makes sense to you. But you may wonder how that information can be translated into a budget for some 15,000 accounts. **Exhibit 14** illustrates how a supply budget might be built using the information you just provided in **Exhibit 13** *(page 91)*. The columns across the top show the natural classes. We are using a fictitious dietary department, so showing only three of the natural classes. You can imagine what the illustration would look like if all 20-30 natural classifications were showing. But the story would be the same.

Row	Description	Formula	Commodities	Food	Forms	Total
	EXHIBIT 14					
1	Prior Year Expense	Input based on history	$100,000	$1,000,000	$27,000	$1,127,000
2	Prior Year Department Volume Statistic	Input based on history	100	100	100	100
3	Prior Year Expense per Dept Volume Statistic	Row 1 / Row 2	$1,000	$10,000	$270	$11,270
4						
5	**Volume Adjustments:**					
6	Prior Year Volume	From Row 2 above	100	100	100	
7	Budget Year Hospital-wide growth %	Input by management	5.00%	5.00%	5.00%	
8	Supply Chain Initiative Natural Class-Specific growth % Adjustment	Input from department matrix	-10.00%	0.00%	0.00%	
9	Department-Specific initiative growth % adjustment	Input from department matrix	0.00%	8.00%	-50.00%	
10	Natural class specific volume statistic	Row 6 x (1 + (Rows 7+8+9))	95	113	55	
11						
12	**Price Adjustments:**					
13	Prior Year average cost per department-specifc Volume Statistic	From Row 3 above	$1,000	$10,000	$270	
14	Natural Class-Specific Expected inflation %	Input from department matrix	1.50%	3.00%	1.00%	
15	Supply chain Pricing-Adjustment initiatives	Input from department matrix	-4.00%	-2.00%	-25.00%	
16	Adjusted Price per Volume Statistic	Row 13 x (1 + (Rows 14+15))	$975.00	$10,100.00	$205.20	
17						
18	Budgeted Supply Expense	Row 10 x Row 16	$92,625	$1,141,300	$11,286	$1,245,211
19	Budgeted overall Department Stat	Input				105
20	Budgeted Supply Expense per Department Stat	Row 18 / Row 19				$11,859

The columns show the natural classes, while the rows show how the process flows. I've numbered each row, and defined the formula for each number in the column labeled "Formula."

Looking at **Exhibit 14**, there are basically four steps to building the budget:

1. Compute the current year supply expense per stat for each natural class. This calculation is illustrated on *rows 1 through 3*. Notice that we use the same stat for all of the natural classes.

2. Starting with the prior year department volume statistic (repeated here on *row 6*, but pulled down from r*ow 2*), we need to adjust the statistic for anticipated volume changes. This adjustment calculation is illustrated on *rows 5 through 10*. There are three ways volume can be impacted:

   a. Budget year hospital-wide growth % *(row 7)*. We are using the Dietary department in this example. If the hospital-wide volume is expected (budgeted) to increase 5%, then on a very simple level, the volume in the department would be expected to increase 5% as well. This adjustment is the same for all natural classes.

b. Changes associated with Supply Chain initiatives *(row 8)*. This information comes from the data you provided in **Exhibit 13** *(page 91)*. Remember again, these changes will usually vary by natural class. In our example (to match **Exhibit 13**), I show that commodities are expected to have a 10% decrease from supply chain initiatives. Notice I have put a zero under food. I did that to illustrate that depending on the initiative, it may or may not apply to multiple natural classes.

c. Changes associated with department-specific growth initiatives *(row 9)*. This too comes from the data you provided in **Exhibit 13**. In our example, I have shown food to increase 8%. Perhaps there is a campaign planned to increase the quality of the food to improve patient satisfaction, which is presumed to increase the number of meals eaten in the cafeteria. I have also shown forms to decrease in volume by 50%. Perhaps new software is budgeted to be installed that will eliminate the use of forms. Once again, it's your story, translated into finance-ese. After setting all of the volume adjustment percentages, a natural class-specific volume statistic is computed *(row 10)*. Notice each natural class' volume statistic may be different at this point. These statistics are only used for supply budgeting, and will not appear in the budget anywhere else. We will talk more about this later. Let's continue with our four steps. On to step 3:

3. Price Adjustments *(row 12)*. Starting with the prior year average cost per department-specific volume statistic (shown on *row 13*, but computed above on *row 3*), there are two ways cost can be impacted:

    a. Natural class-specific expected inflation *(row 14)*. This is the third piece of data pulled from your matrix on **Exhibit 13**.

    b. Supply Chain initiatives related to pricing *(row 15)*. This is the fourth piece of data pulled from your matrix on **Exhibit 13**.

4. Applying the two pricing impact percentages to the prior year actual cost per statistic, a new cost per statistic is calculated *(row 16)*. Notice each natural class has it's own cost per statistic. Now we have all the information we need to compute the budget for each natural class, and the budget for the department in total.

5. Budgeted Supply Expense *(row 18)*. Using the adjusted volume statistic for each natural class on *row 10*, and multiplying it by the inflation and initiative adjusted price per volume statistic on row 16, the budget for each natural class item can be calculated. The sum of the budgets for each natural class will be the budget for the department.

Remember, we discussed earlier in this chapter that the volume calculations used on *row 10* are only for this exercise? The department has a statistic (as has been discussed throughout this book). These numbers on *row 10* have nothing to do with the department statistic—they simply refer to utilization of a particular natural class group of items in the department. Does that make sense? *Row 19* shows the budgeted volume stat for the department. This would be the stat developed using the process defined in **Chapter** 7, and has nothing to do with the stats shown on *row 10*.

Row 20 shows the overall budgeted supply cost per stat for that month, for that department. If this was your department, when you received your final budget from finance, you would see this number in it. If you were to look at your budgeted trial balance, you would also see the dollar amounts shown on row 18 captured in each of the supply sub-accounts.

Once the budgets for each natural class are summed for the department for each month, that total dollar amount is loaded into the department budget. Then, the overall department statistic is divided into the total dollars budgeted to get an average supply cost per department stat. This should be the same as the amount shown on *row 20*. The hospital will also be able to sum the budgets for each natural class across the departments to get a total budget for that natural class. Don't worry: we don't budget twice. This will simply be another way we have to review and monitor actual spending against the budget.

Remember, using the same matrix data from **Exhibit 13** *(page 91)*, this same budgeting exercise illustrated in **Exhibit 14** *(page 93)* must be repeated for each month. Typically, only *row 7* will vary between months (hospital overall growth is not usually budgeted to be the same every month). That variance alone will cause each month supply expense to change. Sometimes a more sophisticated approach to **Exhibit 14** may be used. **Exhibit 14** may be prepared for each month to specifically budget when initiatives are expected to be completed. As you can imagine, it begins to get very complex. But the overall process is the same. So I'll stop here.

And *that* is how supply budgets are done. Much simpler than labor, don't you think? Next we'll wrap up budgeting with the budgeting of fixed operating expenses.

Chapter 9 Self Review Questions

1. Which type of classification are each of the following:
     a. Office supplies
     b. Blood
     c. Antibiotics
     d. Pharmacy
     e. Lab

2. Name the two types of volume initiatives that can impact your supply volume budget.

3. Name the two types of price initiatives that may affect your supply cost budget.

4. If pharmacy supplies were $25,000,000, and supply chain initiatives were being developed to reduce utilization by 5%, and inflation was expected to run 8%, what other information would you need to know to calculate the supply budget
   for pharmacy?

5. If current year lab supply spending was $250,000 on 2,500,000 tests, performed on 100,000 patients, compute next year's supply budget using the following assumptions:
     a. volume is budgeted at 110,000 patients
     b. inflation is 2%
     c. Supply chain initiatives are being designed to reduce utilization by 10% per patient.

Budgeting Other (Fixed) Operating Expenses

Almost done! One last piece to budgeting left. This may be the part of your budget that takes the most of your time, or the least, depending on your hospital. If you work at a very large hospital where things can literally get lost in rounding, then this part of your budget may be done from a very high level. If you work in a smaller hospital where every penny is counted everyday, then this may be the piece of your budget that you are entirely responsible for—and will require many hours of your time.

Let's start by first taking a step back and looking where we've been so far in this section of the book. **Exhibit 15** *(pages 98, 99)* is a sample 12-month budget. Look down the rows on the left side, and you will see the line items that typically show on a budget. Now, as you look at those rows, think about what we have already covered: Gross inpatient and outpatient revenues, revenue deductions, net revenues, salaries, benefits, contract labor, and supplies. Seems like there's a lot left though, huh? And you are probably tired of talking about budgets, aren't you? Relax, actually we are almost done talking about them because all of the remaining items have one thing in common that makes budgeting for them very simple and straightforward—they are *fixed* expenses.

Fixed expenses. What does that mean? Remember in **Chapter 8**, where we discussed variable vs. fixed labor? We talked about fixed labor as being labor that does not fluctuate when volume fluctuates, whereas variable labor should increase or decrease as hospital volumes increase or decrease. The same applies to other expenses as well, and the expenses that we have left to discuss are all *fixed*.

Ok, not totally. I've already said before in this book that nothing is completely fixed, and nothing is completely variable. And that within relevant ranges, *everything* is fixed. Well, what the remaining accounts have in common is that generally, they all have a fairly wide relevant range—much wider than labor or supplies. Large enough that it covers the range of whatever the volumes for the hospital are budgeted to be for the coming year. Maybe I can say this another way that will help clarify. Repairs are considered a fixed expense. That does not mean that repairs at a 100 bed hospital will be the same as repairs at

EXHIBIT 15

J Lee Community Hospital
FY2011 Budget
Radiology

	October	November	December	January	February	March	April	May	June	July	August	September	Total
Revenues:													
Gross Inpatient revenues	$1,240,000	$1,200,000	$1,240,000	$1,240,000	$1,120,000	$1,240,000	$1,200,000	$1,240,000	$1,200,000	$1,280,000	$1,240,000	$1,200,000	$14,640,000
Gross Outpatient revenues	$1,612,000	$1,560,000	$1,612,000	$1,612,000	$1,456,000	$1,612,000	$1,560,000	$1,612,000	$1,560,000	$1,664,000	$1,612,000	$1,560,000	$19,032,000
Total Gross Revenues	$2,852,000	$2,760,000	$2,852,000	$2,852,000	$2,576,000	$2,852,000	$2,760,000	$2,852,000	$2,760,000	$2,944,000	$2,852,000	$2,760,000	$33,672,000
Revenue Deductions	$-	$-	$-		$-	$-	$-	$-	$-	$-	$-	$-	$-
Net Revenues	$2,852,000	$2,760,000	$2,852,000	$2,852,000	$2,576,000	$2,852,000	$2,760,000	$2,852,000	$2,760,000	$2,944,000	$2,852,000	$2,760,000	$33,672,000
Expenses:													
Hospital Salaries	$199,640	$193,200	$199,640	$199,640	$185,730	$205,629	$198,996	$205,629	$198,996	$212,262	$205,629	$198,996	$2,403,988
Contract labor	$-	$-	$-	$-	$-	$-	$-	$-	$-	$-	$-	$-	$-
Benefits	$-	$-	$-	$-	$-	$-	$-	$-	$-	$-	$-	$-	$-
Supplies	$19,821	$19,182	$19,821	$19,821	$17,903	$19,821	$19,182	$19,821	$19,182	$20,461	$19,821	$19,182	$234,020
Maintenance and Repairs	$12,000	$12,000	$12,000	$12,000	$12,000	$12,000	$12,000	$12,000	$12,000	$12,000	$12,000	$12,000	$144,000
Outside Services	$3,200	$3,200	$3,200	$3,200	$3,200	$3,200	$3,200	$3,200	$3,200	$3,200	$3,200	$3,200	$38,400
Rental Expense	$-	$-	$-	$-	$-	$-	$-	$-	$-		$-	$-	$-
Depreciation	$-	$-	$-	$-	$-	$-	$-	$-	$-	$-	$-	$-	$-
Interest	$-	$-	$-	$-	$-	$-	$-	$-	$-	$-	$-	$-	$-
Property Taxes	$-	$-	$-	$-	$-	$-	$-	$-	$-	$-	$-	$-	$-
Insurance	$-	$-	$-	$-	$-	$-	$-	$-	$-	$-	$-	$-	$-
Other Expenses	$1,500	$1,500	$1,500	$1,500	$1,500	$1,500	$1,500	$1,500	$1,500	$1,500	$1,500	$1,500	$18,000
Total Expenses	$236,161	$229,082	$236,161	$236,161	$220,333	$242,151	$234,878	$242,151	$234,878	$249,423	$242,151	$234,878	$2,838,408
Net Margin	$2,615,839	$2,530,918	$2,615,839	$2,615,839	$2,355,667	$2,609,849	$2,525,122	$2,609,849	$2,525,122	$2,694,577	$2,609,849	$2,525,122	$30,833,592

EXHIBIT 15

J Lee Community Hospital
FY2011 Budget
Radiology

	October	November	December	January	February	March	April	May	June	July	August	September	Total
Gross revenue per stat	$400.00	$400.00	$400.00	$400.00	$400.00	$400.00	$400.00	$400.00	$400.00	$400.00	$400.00	$400.00	$400.00
Inpatient stat	3,100	3,000	3,100	3,100	2,800	3,100	3,000	3,100	3,000	3,200	3,100	3,000	36,600
Outpatient Stat	4,030	3,900	4,030	4,030	3,640	4,030	3,900	4,030	3,900	4,160	4,030	3,900	47,580
Total Stat	7,130	6,900	7,130	7,130	6,440	7,130	6,900	7,130	6,900	7,360	7,130	6,900	84,180
Labor Cost per Stat	$28.00	$28.00	$28.00	$28.00	$28.84	$28.84	$28.84	$28.84	$28.84	$28.84	$28.84	$28.84	$28.56
Supply Cost per Stat	$2.78	$2.78	$2.78	$2.78	$2.78	$2.78	$2.78	$2.78	$2.78	$2.78	$2.78	$2.78	$2.78
Worked MH/Stat	1.05	1.05	1.05	1.05	1.05	1.05	1.05	1.05	1.05	1.05	1.05	1.05	1.05
Paid MH/Stat	1.16	1.16	1.16	1.16	1.16	1.16	1.16	1.16	1.16	1.16	1.16	1.16	1.16
OT%	2.50%	2.50%	2.50%	2.50%	2.50%	2.50%	2.50%	2.50%	2.50%	2.50%	2.50%	2.50%	2.50%
Paid Hours	8,235	7,970	8,235	8,235	7,438	8,235	7,970	8,235	7,970	8,501	8,235	7,970	97,228
Hospital FTEs	46.62	46.62	46.62	46.62	46.62	46.62	46.62	46.62	46.62	48.12	46.62	46.62	46.74
Contract Labor FTEs	-	-	-	-	-	-	-	-	-	-	-	-	-
AHR hospital	$24.24	$24.24	$24.24	$24.24	$24.97	$24.97	$24.97	$24.97	$24.97	$24.97	$24.97	$24.97	$24.73
AHR contract labor	$-	$-	$-	$-	$-	$-	$-	$-	$-	$-	$-	$-	$-

a 1,000 bed hospital. But within the hospital that YOU work in, the volume doesn't change enough over the course of the year (unless you have construction going on) to increase or decrease repair expense. So *within that volume range,* repairs will not be affected by movements in patient volumes. That makes them a fixed expense.

What all is included in fixed expenses? If you look at **Exhibit 15** *(pages 98, 99)*, you will see the example line items I have reflected as fixed expense lines: Maintenance and Repairs, Outside services, Rentals, Depreciation, Interest, Property Taxes, Insurance, and Other Expenses. Please note that these are my own example. Every hospital will be different. The names may be different, and some items may not show up at all. If you work for an investor-owned hospital, depreciation will definitely not be included. My point is that, going back to the discussion in **Chapter 3** on the *General Ledger,* every hospital sets up its own accounts to fit its needs, and what makes sense to them. It is important that there be sound reasons behind how accounts are grouped for financial statement presentation, but within reason, they may do whatever they want. There is no "rule book" that defines the Chart of Accounts or governs how accounts are presented. So going back to the question of what is included in fixed expenses—working backwards, you could say that fixed expenses are the expenses remaining after labor (including salaries, benefits and contract labor), supplies and bad debt. They may consist of many line items, but remember, for most hospitals they will only add up to around 25% of total expenses.

Budgeting for fixed expenses is very straightforward for two reasons.

First, as we just said, although there may be many accounts, each individual account is probably relatively small, and since budgets are always meant to be estimates, if an individual fixed account that is small is budgeted incorrectly, it won't materially affect the accuracy of the overall budget.

Second, most of the accounts are either very simple to accurately budget, or virtually impossible. A maintenance contract on your MRI is very simple. You probably already have a contract, and you pay a fixed fee every month that covers 90% of the things that may go wrong. Or you have an annual license inspection that has a fixed fee and always comes up for renewal in August. Easy. Repairs, on the other hand, are completely unpredictable. You never know what will need repair or when. That makes budgeting little more than a guess based on historical experience.

Enough talk about "what" and "why" of fixed expenses. Let's dig into "how" to budget them.

There is really only one approach. What will vary from hospital to hospital is the level of detail that is compiled. These budgets may be prepared at the "Account level" or at the "Vendor level." Which approach is used will determine how much work you are required to do. Either way, this part of the budget may well be the one where you have the most input, and/or are required to be the most involved. Why? Because these accounts are fixed, so by definition, most of them do not change with volume. For most of these accounts, the amount you spend, and when you spend it are both completely independent of anything else going on around the hospital.

For example, the timing and amount you pay to renew your license and accreditation in your Lab has nothing to do with how many patients you are seeing in the department. It is probably a one-time expense, once a year—or maybe even once every three years. Some "fixed" expenses do have a loose connection to hospital or department volumes. Equipment rentals are an example of that. If your hospital rents specialty mattresses for specific patients, then the volume of rentals actually depends upon how many of *those* patients the hospital sees in a given month. History may tell you that "on average" you see (hypothetically) 50 of those patients each month. But you may also know that during certain times of the year, the volume of those patients tends to be higher (regardless of whether overall hospital volume is higher or lower), and/or that when the hospital volumes goes up, these rentals tend to go up as well. You can see that because of the many unique issues with many of these accounts, they do not lend themselves to modeling or to an automated template to budget them. To budget them appropriately, you actually need to handle them manually. That's where you come in as the best person to know the details for these accounts. Finance will help you of course!

Let's start with the approach that will be very simple and not require much time from you—the "Account level" approach. The advantage to this approach is that is can be done relatively quickly. The disadvantage is that you may not end up with a very accurate budget, and if you use this approach and want a more accurate budget, it can be messy to get there because you will need to manually intervene and override the high-level approach.

Look at **Exhibit 16** *(page 102)*. Down the left side, you will notice that this Exhibit looks very similar to **Exhibit 1** *(page 22)* from **Chapter 3** (although it shows different accounts). These are sample accounts for a few fixed expense items that you may be budgeting for. Don't worry if your hospital, or your department would use different accounts. The concepts will be the same.

Look across the columns at the top. As always, I have numbered them, and the row below that shows the formulas for each column. Let's walk through this one step at a time together.

1. *YTD Actual:* this column shows the actual year to date expenses that have been incurred. This data will be given to you.

2. *Prorated portion of column 1:* Columns 2 and 3 show two different approaches that can be taken to estimate what the expense will be during the remaining three months of the year in order to get to a 12-month

EXHIBIT 16

Column #	1	2	3	4	5	6	7	8	9
Formula	Input by Finance	(Col 1/9 x 3)	Input by Finance	Input	Col 1 + either col 2 or col 3	Input	col 5 + col 6	col 7 / 12	Input
	YTD Actual through 9 months	Prorated Portion of Column 1	Budget for 3 remaining months	Choice: col 2 or col 3	12 Month Projected Amount	Inflation or Other Change	12 month Budget Amount	Assumed Budget per month	Notes
6000.00 Maintenance & Repairs									
6010.00 Maintenance Contracts									
6010.10 Bio-Med Equipment	$900,000	$300,000	$250,000	2	$1,200,000	$-	$1,200,000	$100,000	
6010.20 IT Hardware	$2,000,000	$666,667	$1,000,000	2	$2,666,667	$300,000	$2,966,667	$247,222	
6010.30 IT Software	$4,500,000	$1,500,000	$1,500,000	2	$6,000,000	$1,000,000	$7,000,000	$583,333	
6020.00 Repairs									
6020.10 Parts	$1,000,000	$333,333	$120,000	2	$1,333,333	$26,667	$1,360,000	$113,333	
6020.20 Labor	$1,350,000	$450,000	$200,000	2	$1,800,000	$36,000	$1,836,000	$153,000	
7000.00 Outside Services									
7020.00 Clinical Services									
7020.10 Reference Lab	$1,800,000	$600,000	$300,000	2	$2,400,000	$120,000	$2,520,000	$210,000	
7020.20 Imaging	$-	$-	$200,000	2	$-		$-	$-	
7030.00 License and Inspection									
7030.10 JCAHO	$270,000	$90,000	$90,000	2	$360,000		$360,000	$30,000	
7030.20 CAP	$50,000	$16,667	$-	3	$50,000	$5,000	$55,000	$4,583	All $55k in November
7030.30 State License Fees	$-	$-	$75,000	3	$75,000	$10,000	$85,000	$7,083	All $85k in March

total projected expense. The amount shown in column 2 is based on a very simple formula: column 1 / 9 x 3. Since column 1 reflects nine months of data, dividing by 9 gives an average expense per month. Since there are three months remaining, the number is multiplied by 3 to get a projected total remaining expense for the remaining 3 months of the year. This approach can yield an inaccurate 12-month projection if you have expenses that do not occur ratably throughout the year. Look at the 7030 accounts (License and Inspections). These expenses frequently are a one-time expense during the year. Perhaps you have a once-a-year contract renewal fee that occurs in the last month of the year. Account 7030.30 reflects this scenario. Since it has not happened in the first nine months, using this approach, it will not be included in the projected remainder. Which means it would not be included in next year's budget. This is a very common mistake in budgeting of fixed expenses.

3. *The remaining budget:* This column reflects the second alternative for projecting remaining expenses for the year. If there are three months left, this column would be populated with the budget for those months. Following this approach is designed to avoid the problem discussed in 2. above, where you have a once-a-year expense that hasn't happened yet (but hopefully you budgeted it to happen later, so using this approach, the expense *will* populate in this column). Again, account 7030.30 is an example where this is a better approach. So is account 7030.20. In that case, the expense has happened, so no further expense needs to be added to the 12-month projection. But this approach can also lead to it's own problems. If something significant has changed, your monthly expenses for some of these accounts may be dramatically different than the budget that was prepared a year ago, so populating the projected remainder with the budget may not be even close to what you think will actually happen. Accounts 6010.10 and 6010.20 are two examples where using the budget for the remainder of the year yields a significantly different number than using a prorated portion of column 1. In the case of account 6010.10, the actual monthly average is running *more* than the remaining budget ($300,000 vs $250,000), whereas account 6010.20 has the opposite situation. The prorated portion of column 1 is less than the remaining budget ($666,667 vs $1,000,000).

4. *Choice:* column 2 or column 3 - This column would be populated by you. Here, you would indicate whether the amount shown in column 2 is a better approximation of what you expect to happen during the remaining 3 months, or column 3 is better.

5. *12-month Projected Amount:* This column is a formula. It adds together column 1 (the actual expense for the first nine months of the year) plus whichever column 2 or 3 you recommended as the best choice for projecting the remainder. The sum of the 2 numbers yields a 12-month

projection for the year. This amount then becomes the baseline, or starting point, for budgeting next year.

6. *Inflation or other change:* this column should be populated by you, based on your experience and knowledge. There is no science to this column. I've shown a few example scenarios using the different accounts:

   a. Account 6010.10—I show no change. Perhaps you have a multi-year contract with an outside company that provides for a fixed monthly fee and there is no inflation/fee increase clause. So you know this amount will not increase.

   b. Account 6010.20—I show a large change. Perhaps you bought some new equipment that will need a new maintenance contract next year.

   c. Account 6010.30—I show a large change. Perhaps you have a go-live on some new software between now and year end, so new license fees will be due next year.

   d. Accounts 6020.10 and 6020.20—I added 2% inflation.

   e. Account 7020.10—I show a 5% increase. Even though this is considered a Fixed Expense, in fact, it probably moves with volume. In my scenario, if hospital volume is budgeted to increase 5%, you would want to probably increase this account by the same amount. Also, you may want to add an inflation factor to this account, unless you have a contract.

   f. Accounts 7030.20 and 7030.30—I show large increases. Perhaps you have received a letter notifying you of these increases.

7. *12-Month Budget Amount:* This column is simply a formula adding columns 5 +6 together.

8. *Assumed budget per month:* unless it is manually changed, most hospitals budget fixed expenses ratably over the year, by computing the budget for the entire year, then budgeting 1/12th of it each month. That is what this column shows.

9. *Input:* this column is where you might indicate that the budget should NOT be simply spread over 12 months, but instead put in a particular month. I demonstrate this in accounts 7030.20 and 7030.30.

The other approach to budgeting fixed expenses follows the same concepts I've shown in **Exhibit 16** *(page 102)*, except that instead of just walking through the process for each G/L account, you do it for each *vendor within each account*. As you can imagine, this process would be much more time consuming. It is a more accurate and precise way to budget, but for most hospitals, the increase in accuracy is not worth the substantial increase in time required to prepare the budget at this level, and unless yours is a smaller hospital, it may not even be feasible.

Chapter 10 Self Review Questions

1. Name three common fixed expenses.

2. If your hospital outsources a patient service, such as interpreting, should that expense be budgeted as a fixed or a variable expense?

3. Even though repairs can vary greatly from month to month, and from hospital to hospital, they are considered to be a fixed expense. Why?

4. If you have a once-a-year expense that typically occurs in the last month of the year, which approach will be best for preparing the forecast for the remainder of the year to ensure that item is captured?

5. If your department spending on forms has totaled $100,000 through 10 months of the year, and the remaining budget is $10,000, will applying the prorated approach to forecast the remainder of the year yield an accurate baseline for next year's budget?

Section III

Monitoring During the Month

Know Your Budget

It's the first day of the month. Do you know your budget for the month? As a good manager, you should—not every detail, but at least a few key pieces of information that are important to your department. Things you will want to have in your head to monitor each week, if not every day. To do that, you must have a copy of your budget. Do you?

Before the budget year starts, as soon as the budget is finished, make sure you receive a copy of the budget for your department. At a minimum, you need the following information for *each month:*

1. The volume statistic for the department, if there is one (remember if you are an overhead, or fixed department, you may not have one).

2. A budgeted income or Profit and Loss Statement for your department. This report will show revenues (separated between inpatient and outpatient), salaries, contract labor, supplies, and other expenses such as maintenance and repairs, rental fees, consulting fees, seminars and education, etc. See **Exhibit 15** *(pages 98, 99)* for an example of one. We will go over it in a minute. If you are given a budget that you did not help prepare, ask for as much detail as possible.

3. Labor management budgets. Monitoring these will be discussed at length in **Chapter 13**. For now, you just need to know that as part of your budget package, this is information you should receive. Ideally, the information you receive should include:

    a. Worked and paid FTEs. Worked FTEs should be divided between employed and contract FTEs

    b. Worked and Paid Man Hours/Stat

    c. Non-Productive hours or %

    d. The Average Hourly Rate (AHR) for the department split between employed and contract labor

    e. Overtime hours and/or OT percentages

f. Call and Callback hours or percentages

g. Cost per Unit of Service

4. A detail of your supply budget. This detail may be a trial balance showing the budget for each natural class of expense. You will also need to know what your supply budget per stat is.

5. Any detail support behind your other expenses.

6. A copy of the capital budget for your department showing what items were approved, for how much, and when they may be purchased.

I realize that seems like an overwhelming list. How in the world can you possibly keep all this straight? Don't worry, we're going to spend the next few chapters breaking it all down for you. And by the way, you won't need to keep all this information in your head all the time. You just need to *have* it. So you can refer to it as you need to. In order to be able to actually *use* it, you need to understand it.

Therefore, let's take a look at the sample budget shown in **Exhibit 15** *(pages 98, 99)*. The sample budget shown has much of the information you want. I illustrated it this way so that if you do not receive it, you will know what to ask for (and what it should look like). Spend a few minutes familiarizing yourself with **Exhibit 15**. When you're ready, let's walk through it.

OK . . . here are some key things to note—things you will want to review when you get your own budget:

1. Notice this is a *monthly* budget. If your budget comes in a different format, you at least need to know what each individual month's budget is. Even if they need to give you a separate sheet of paper for each month. The column on the left is the first month of the hospital's fiscal year. Notice that it may not be January. The federal government's fiscal year begins October 1 each year. Since so much of a hospital's revenues come from the government, many hospitals use the same fiscal year ("FY").

2. Going down the rows on the left, you see the budget for both inpatient and outpatient revenues. Your department may not have revenues at all if you are a support or overhead department—or you may only have one or the other. For example, if your hospital has a separate department for Outpatient Surgery, then that department will not have any inpatient revenue.

3. Notice that the "Revenue Deductions" row is blank. Remember from **Chapter 2** that revenue deductions are not charged to the individual departments. We'll come back to why you need to be aware of this in a moment.

4. Next are the expenses. Your hospital's order and grouping may vary slightly, but you will almost certainly see rows for salaries and supplies.

Other rows may vary by hospital. The dollars themselves aren't very meaningful without the data behind them. Those are the things we will talk about in later chapters—looking behind those numbers to see what story they tell.

5. Look at the row labeled "Net Margin." It probably looks rather large to you. At least it should. In this example, the revenues shown are over $33 million for the year, and expenses are only $2.8 million. Wow! If hospitals were really that profitable, everyone would be in the business! But they aren't. So why does this budget imply that it is? Go back to point #3 above about there being no Revenue Deductions shown in the department. If you don't remember why, you can refresh your memory in **Chapter 2**. So how much money DOES this department really make? It's hard to say. Remember that most inpatient business is paid a fixed fee, regardless of how long a patient stays or how many services the patient receives. So if a physician orders a chest X-ray daily for a patient that stays 10 days, the Radiology Department looks very busy, and has a lot of revenues, but the payment the hospital receives may only be based on one X-ray. So for the other nine X-rays, the department incurred the cost *but the hospital did not get paid at all.* The only point you need to take away from here is that you must understand that the Net Margin you see each month on your department's financial statements is *not* meaningful or real.

6. Underneath the Net Margin, I have added some metrics and statistics. These may or may not be included on your budget report. If they aren't, they can most likely be provided to you, perhaps as a separate report. Feel free to ask for it if you need it.

7. Notice the Gross Revenue per stat. For this example, I used a simple $400 amount. Your number (if you have one) will likely be something less consistent. Remember our discussion in **Chapter 2** about the hospital's Charge Description Master (CDM)? How there is a different price for everything the hospital does? So in the Radiology Department, there are hundreds of different exams done. Each has it's own price. This number is simply a *blended average* of your gross charges for all the things you do in your department. The number used for budgeting is probably based on the prior year's blended average. It is calculated by simply dividing gross revenues by the total number of exams performed. Some departments may have different rates for inpatient and outpatient services—that is more a function of how your budget software works than anything else.

8. Look at the volume statistics in this report. For simplicity, I set this example to be at 100 inpatient procedures per calendar day. You will surely discover that your budget fluctuates based on the number of days in the month. Especially February. Volumes, revenues, and labor and

supplies should all be lower at least in February, and (predictably) also lower in the months with 30 days compared to the months with 31 days.

9. Labor and supply costs per stat. These are simply calculated by dividing the respective costs by the volume for the month. We will talk more about that calculation and managing these later.

Now that you are comfortable reading a budget, look at your own. When you first receive it, review it carefully. Make sure you understand it. If you don't, make an appointment with someone in finance to discuss it. Don't be afraid to ask questions. Remember, you no longer have reason to be intimidated or overwhelmed when looking at all these numbers. This is simply *finance-ese* telling *your* story, the story of what *your* department is expected to achieve next year. You cannot manage or achieve what you don't know or understand. If I were you, I would schedule a meeting to go over your budget. I would prepare for that meeting in the following way:

1. Obtain the copy of next year's budget, including as much of the detail outlined above as possible.

2. Obtain the same information for the year just getting ready to end (or maybe has just ended).

3. Compare the two side by side—first in total, then month by month. There may in fact be a report that finance can give you that does this comparison for you. Make notes.

   a. How does volume compare (if applicable). If your department is an overhead, or support department, you need to know how the overall volume of the hospital is budgeted compared to the prior year. For example, if the hospital volume is expected to grow, and you are in charge of the HIM (Hospital Information Management) department that manages patient Medical Records, you may need a budget that includes an increase in your staff.

   b. How do salaries compare? Was a merit increase budgeted? If so, when? Does the Average Hourly Rate reflect an increase to compensate?

   c. What assumptions were used to build the labor budgets compared to the prior year actual numbers for things like worked and paid FTEs, non-productive time percentages, contract labor, overtime, callback, MH/stat? If they have changed significantly, is there already a plan for achieving the change, or are you responsible for finding a way to achieve it? You'll probably feel more comfortable having these conversations after you complete **Chapter 13** on Labor Management.

d. What assumptions were used to build the supply budgets? What inflation was built in, what information was it based on, and how does that compare with what you hear in your professional circles (e.g. pharmacists typically know what changes are expected in drug pricing)? Are there cost saving initiatives built in? If so, are there plans for achieving these savings, or are you supposed to find a way to make them happen?

e. How do other expenses compare to prior years? Are there changes that will occur this year that you know will either increase or decrease these expenses? If so—does the budget reflect those changes? For example, you may be in charge of a department that has a license or certification renewal every three years. If that expense was incurred last year, you will not need to budget it next year. Or vice-versa: if the expense was *not* incurred last year, but will occur this year, it needs to be added.

f. How does the capital budget compare to the list of items you requested? What did *not* get included? Are those items things you can live without? If you don't think so, why not? And how can the issue be addressed? Is there a work-around you will need to do? Discuss it with Administration now.

These are all very fair questions to ask. Of course, in a perfect world, you participated in the preparation of your budget. So you already know the answers to all these questions. If so—*great!* If not, at least now you know how to arm yourself. So now that you understand how to read your budget, let's start *using* it! Doesn't that sound fun? No? Aw . . . give me a chance, at least?

Chapter 11 Self Review Questions

1. Name the six key pieces of information you need to get a copy of when the budget has been completed.

2. If you are a revenue-generating department, why does your department Profit and Loss statement usually look as though you make a lot of money?

3. If you don't understand some things in your budget when you receive it, what should you do?

4. What is the simplest way to get a quick handle on what changes there are in your budget?

5. Why is it important to review your approved capital budget together with your operating budget?

Monitoring Volume

I said in the last chapter that you did not need to carry your entire budget around in your head, but instead just a few key pieces of information. This chapter is devoted to Volume. Why would I devote an entire chapter to volume? Because *volume is the single most important statistic to know and carry around in your head*. Why is volume so important? Because it probably drives 100% of your revenue, and over 50% of your expenses. It is the single largest indicator of how you are doing financially.

On the first day of every month (if not earlier), I recommend you get your budget out and look up your volume budget for the month. I also recommend you find out what the hospital's overall volume budget is. Let's talk about why you need to know this and what you do with that information. Let's start with the hospital as a whole first.

HOSPITAL VOLUME

I recommend that you, as a good manager, know what the hospital's *budgeted volume* statistic is. Then, during the month you should be paying attention to how well the hospital is doing against that target. Your hospital probably has one overarching statistic that they use as an acid test of how they are doing. It will vary by hospital. Many hospitals use census or patient days.

For me, the strongest indicator of how well my hospital is doing is Adjusted Discharges. Why? On The inpatient side, most payors now pay on a per-discharge basis for inpatient business, so the volume of discharges is a better indicator to me of how much inpatient revenue I am generating (and therefore how many dollars of expenses I can support) than is census. Does that make sense to you? And by using adjusted discharges, I also get an indication of how I am doing on the outpatient side of the business. Confusing? Maybe a simple illustration will help.

Let's look at the inpatient side first.

Notice that in **Exhibit 17** *(page 116)*, both the Budgeted and Actual columns have the same average daily census. But there is a very big difference

EXHIBIT 17			
	Actual	Budget	Difference
Inpatient Discharges	1,136	1,483	(347)
x Average Length of Stay	4.70	3.60	1.10
= Total Patient Days	5,340	5,340	-
/ Days in Month	30	30	-
= Average Daily Census	178	178	-
Average Reimbursement per Inpatient Discharge	$10,000	$10,000	$-
x Inpatient Discharges	1,136	1,483	(347)
Total Reimbursement	$11,361,702	$14,833,333	$(3,471,631)
Labor Costs per Patient Day	$500	$500	$-
x Patient Days	5,340	5,340	-
= Total Labor Cost	$2,670,000	$2,670,000	$-
Net	$8,691,702	$12,163,333	$(3,471,631)

in how that census was generated. The actual month had 347 fewer patients discharged, but those patients stayed an average of 1.10 days longer than the Budgeted month, resulting in the same number of patient days and average daily census!

Why does that matter? Because the hospital will be paid *per discharge* for most of those patients, *not per day*. So *days* don't matter—discharges do. With the same average census, the hospital will incur the same labor costs, but revenue will be lower. If the hospital averages $10,000 of reimbursement per inpatient discharge, then those 347 patients would have generated $3.47 *million* of extra revenue to cover the same costs!

"Huh?" you say? Look further down to the labor costs. On the labor side, the costs are the same. It is *all about the days* on the labor side. The patient must be cared for every day. So when discharges are down, even though census is the same, and therefore the costs are the same, the revenue is less. So the hospital is making less money.

The hospital budget will include a budget for discharges, length of stay, and census. This example illustrates that if I only monitored census, I could be misled as to how I was doing during the month. And that is why I consider discharges a better measure during the month of how the hospital is doing on the inpatient side against budget.

To pull outpatient volumes into the measurement, I recommend *adjusted* discharges. If you don't remember what an adjusted discharge is, please see

EXHIBIT 18			
	Actual	Budget	Difference
Inpatient Discharges	1,136	1,483	(347)
Adjustment Factor	1.80	1.50	0.30
Adjusted Discharges	2,045	2,225	(180)
Average Reimbursement per Adjusted Discharge	$6,000	$6,000	$-
	$12,268,800	$13,347,000	$(1,078,200)

Chapter 1. Sometimes inpatient volume can be under budget, but outpatient volumes are compensating for at least part of that shortfall. Remember in **Exhibit 17** that inpatient discharges were projected to be 347 less than budget, resulting in a revenue shortfall of $3.47M? Let's layer on the impact of outpatient volume and revenue to that illustration.

Look at **Exhibit 18**.

Notice that the inpatient discharge numbers here are the same as in **Exhibit 17**. But notice that the Adjustment Factor is greater than budget. Please refer back to **Chapter 1** if you want a refresher on how the Adjustment Factor is calculated. Suffice to say here that in this example, when the Adjustment Factor is greater than budget, it means that the outpatient volumes are greater than budget. So Adjusted Discharges are only 180 less than budget.

Next, notice that in **Exhibit 18** the Average Reimbursement per Adjusted Discharge is only $6,000, whereas in **Exhibit 17**, the Average Reimbursement per Inpatient Discharge was $10,000. Why? Remember that Adjusted Discharges incorporate both inpatient and outpatient volumes — it is a *blended* number. Therefore, the reimbursement per adjusted discharge is also a blended number. Outpatient reimbursement is much less than inpatient reimbursement (because it has a lower cost). So the illustration here shows a blended average of $6,000 per Adjusted Discharge.

Now compare the $1,078,200 reimbursement shortfall in **Exhibit 18** against the $3.47 million reimbursement shortfall shown in **Exhibit 17**. See how the outpatient volume being ahead of budget has partially compensated for the inpatient volume shortfall? That is why I prefer to use Adjusted Discharges to monitor hospital-wide volumes during the month against budget.

If your hospital's daily report does not include Adjusted Discharges, then I recommend you monitor inpatient discharges. As you can see by **Exhibit 18**, even when the outpatient volume was substantially ahead of volume (as indicated by the adjustment factor being 1.80 against a budget of 1.50), that volume increase could still not completely compensate for the inpatient shortfall. So if inpatient volume is behind, although outpatient volume may shrink (or increase) that shortfall partially, it is difficult for outpatient volume to completely compensate for inpatient shortfalls. The reverse is also true: if inpatient volume is over budget, even if outpatient volume is behind budget, it is difficult for it to be so far behind as to "wipe out" the favorable inpatient variance. Why? Because outpatient revenue has a much lower margin than inpatient revenue. Both reimbursement and costs are lower. So unless you want to be very ambitious and apply the formulas from **Chapter 1** each day, then I recommend simply monitoring inpatient discharge volume against budget if your hospital does not report adjusted discharges each day.

So why is it important for you to know and monitor your hospital's primary volume indicator? How does what the rest of the hospital is doing affect you and your department? Just like patient days (or census) may not be a good indicator of overall hospital performance, your department indictor may not reflect the rest of the hospital. Let's say for example that you are in charge of MRI. Volume in your department may be up simply because a new physician in the area has begun sending his patients over for outpatient MRIs. Good for your department, but if the hospital is empty, the burst of volume in your department isn't going to generate enough revenue to cover the fixed overhead expenses in the other departments.

You probably have budgeted expenses in your department that are not absolutely mandatory. Or perhaps they are mandatory but do not need to happen this month. Just a few examples: seminars, consulting fees, filling vacancies in the department. If the hospital overall is not performing at budgeted levels, as a member of the management team, you have a fiscal responsibility to do your part in adjusting spending downward to match the lower anticipated revenue.

Most hospitals have some sort of daily report showing volumes for the entire hospital. This report is something you, as a good manager, should look at each day and see how volumes are against budget. So how do you do that? There are two approaches you can use.

1. You can look at the volumes each day against a "daily" budget indicator. This is a very simple approach, and is easy to do. All you need to know is the budgeted indicator for the month. Let's use the budget shown in **Exhibits 17** and **18** *(pages 116, 117)*: inpatient discharges budgeted for the month are 1,483. As shown on **Exhibit 17**, there are 30 days in the month. That means, on average, the hospital is expecting 49.43 discharges each calendar day of the month (1,483 / 30 = 49.43). For simplicity, let's round the number to 50. At the beginning of the month, you would calculate this number. Just once. Then you keep the number 50 in your head, and each day when the hospital's daily volume report comes out you look at the discharge number for the day. Is it more or less than 50? If more, then the hospital beat budget that day. And if, over the course of the month, there are more days greater than 50 than

days less than 50, then the hospital is probably ahead of budget. The great thing about this approach is that it is so simple. Once you establish the "50 discharges" number, you don't need a pen or paper again. You simply look at the number each day and compare. The weakness in this approach is that you can be misled. For example, if the hospital had two days of 51 discharges but one day of 40 discharges, then even though two out of three days were "greater than 50," the hospital is still behind budget. So, if you choose to use this method, just know that.

2. To project the volume statistic for the month, you need to know only four things:

a. The hospital's month-to-date statistic (e.g. discharges or adjusted discharges)

b. The date the statistic is reported through. For example, on July 18th, the report may be released showing discharges month-to-date through July 17th)

c. The statistic budget for the month (e.g. budgeted discharges or adjusted discharges)

d. The number of days in the current month (e.g. there are 31 days in July)

Using the month-to-date statistic, you want to project what the total will be for the month, and compare that projection to the budget. The formula to do that is:

The MTD statistic *divided by*
the date the statistic is reported through
times
the number of days in the month
or
a. *divided by* b. *times* d.

For example, let's say you have the following information:

- 722 discharges (month-to-date statistic)
- July 17th (date statistic is reported through)
- 1,600 (budgeted statistic for the month)
- 31 days (July has 31 days in it)

Then the projected number of the discharges for the month is:

722 divided by 17 x 31 = 1,317. Since the budget is 1,600, you can quickly conclude that if things continue at the rate they are going, the hospital is going to miss its volume budget significantly.

As you can see, this is a more complex approach to monitoring the hospital's volume during the month than approach 1. I recommend a combination. Use approach 1 daily, but "true it up" by applying approach 2 maybe once a week.

So why do you need to do this? You aren't the CFO. You are only responsible for your department, right? As a good manager and member of the hospital management team, I would say no. I would say you ARE responsible for contributing to the success of the entire hospital. How should you do that? Let's talk about that.

Going back to the numbers used in approach 2, If the projected discharges are 1,317, and the budgeted discharges are 1,600, then based on this information, the hospital will miss discharges by 283 discharges (1,600—1,317), which is 18%. All else being equal, if discharges are off 18%, the hospital would therefore be expecting to miss revenue by roughly 18% as well. If the hospital revenue is 18% less than budget, then unless expenses can be reduced by an equal amount, the monthly financial performance will not achieve budget.

So as a responsible member of the management TEAM, what contribution can you make to reducing expenses? Can you defer some things? Can you reduce your labor expenses? We'll talk about that in the next chapter.

DEPARTMENT VOLUME

If your department generates its own volume statistic, you should always know what volume your department is budgeted for. Registrations, surgeries, lab tests, patient days, etc.

As previously mentioned, on the first day of the month, get your budget out and check your volume statistic for the month. A really seasoned manager will actually do this exercise mid-month during previous month. When we talk about why you do this exercise, and what you do with the information, you'll see why it is actually better to do it earlier. Whenever you pull this information, do two things with it:

1. Compare that budgeted volume to the most recent month's actual volume. How does it compare?

   a. Does the budget reflect more volume that you experienced last month? If so, how much more? Is there a reason you believe there *will* be more volume? Perhaps you run the OB department, and you are coming into what is a traditionally busy month for you. Maybe the budget reflects an increase because a new piece of equipment was slated to be in place which would increase capacity? If so, did that happen?

   b. Does the budget reflect *less* volume than you experienced last month? If so, how much less? Is there a reason you believe there will be less volume? Again, perhaps the opposite is true now in an OB department—perhaps you are coming out of your busy time.

2. Divide the budgeted volume by the number of business days in the month for you. For some departments that are open 24/7, that will be

simply the number of days in the month. For other departments—that are not open 7 days a week—you will want to divide by the number of days that you are open. For example, many hospitals only do emergency surgery on the weekends. So the "hours of business" for the Surgery Department are really Monday through Friday, which means (other than the emergency surgeries on weekends), they only generate volume on 20 to 22 days each month (depending on how the days fall that month). Whatever your situation, after you have divided the number, your result is the average volume your department needs to achieve each day that it is open in order to achieve budget for the month. Let's take an OB department as an example. If your department statistic is deliveries, and the budget is 300 for the month, in a month when there are 30 days, then to achieve budget, you need to achieve volumes averaging 10 deliveries per day (300/30 = 10). Once you have the number, tuck it in your head to carry around. Thereafter, each day, you have an "acid test" as to how you are doing against budget. On days when deliveries exceed 10, you know you had a good day. When deliveries are less than 10, you know you need to be cautious. More on that in a moment.

So now that you know your budget for the month, and have locked a daily volume stat in your head, what do you do next? Whether you do this mid-month the previous month, or the first day of the current month, after you've answered question #1 above, ask yourself "How well positioned am I to achieve budget for the month?"

- Is volume budgeted to be higher than last month? If so, do I know where that volume is going to come from?

- If I DO expect volume to be higher, have I scheduled staffing adequately to cover the increased volume?

- Whether volume is expected to be higher or lower, who is expected to be out for vacation, FMLA, etc? Am I prepared?

- If budgeted volume is higher than the most recent month actual volume, what steps can I take to reduce my expenses this month to offset the expected less-than-budgeted volume? Remember, your labor budget is based on budgeted volume. If your department is budgeted as a "variable" department, you are expected to be able to flex down. So if budgeted volume is set at (say) 7,000 X-rays, using 47 FTEs, and you see no reason to believe volume will come in any higher than the 6,000 you did last month, then you need to be ready to also use less-than-budgeted FTEs. (we'll discuss this much more in the next chapter).

- If I do not believe I will achieve the budgeted volume this month, are there other expenses that were budgeted that I can defer, such as reducing rentals, or travel and education?

We'll talk more about actually monitoring these items later, but for now, you should just be *planning*—planning ahead for the month—thinking about these things. Putting actions into motion based on what you see or anticipate occurring. As a manager, *it is your job to manage to the volume you actually experience and to find ways to still achieve your budget (or exceed it!) regardless of whether or not your budgeted volume materializes.* Remember, if the volume does not occur, then the revenue will not materialize. If the revenue does not materialize, then the money available to cover the expenses is less, and expenses need to be flexed down to the revenue levels that are being achieved.

You can see that some of the actions you may need to take will need to be taken before the first day of the month. That is why I recommend you perform this exercise mid-month the previous month. This will give you more time to adjust staffing schedules up or down, cancel or postpone approving seminars, travel, etc.

Chapter 12 Self Review Questions

1. What is the single most important statistic to know and carry around in your head?

2. When would a seasoned manager look at the February budget to see what the February budgeted volume is to be?

3. Why are hospital discharges a better volume indicator than census?

4. Why is it important to look at hospital volume in addition to department volume?

5. If discharges month-to-date through the 18th of a 30 day month are 600, and the budget for the month is 980, is the hospital trending to end the month ahead of budget, behind budget, or right on budget?

Labor Management

Labor Management. Dirty words to some, words that send shivers down the spine of others. Whether your hospital monitors it daily, weekly, at the end of each pay period, or not until the end of the month (increasingly rare these days), it is, as we've discussed, the single largest expense most hospitals have, *and* the most controllable. Which means it likely gets the most attention.

As a great manager, just as you saw in the volume budget discussion in the previous chapter, when you look at your volume budget for the month, you want to check the key labor management metrics as well. You should always know what your key labor management budgeted metrics are for that month (as applicable):

- MH/stat. Either worked or paid, whichever you are responsible for if you are budgeted as a variable department

- Worked or Paid FTEs if you are budgeted as a fixed, support, or overhead department

- Budgeted Overtime %

- Budgeted contract labor (if any)

- Budgeted callback % (if applicable)

You hate to see that email or get that voicemail from your boss saying he needs to talk to you about your department's labor productivity/management. Take a deep breath. Are you ready to tackle this topic? I promise—it's not really that bad. You're a good manager, right? A smart person? You must be, or you wouldn't be in your position. Like most things that seem scary at first, if you can break it down, understand the pieces, then you can step back and realize it's not that scary after all: you can do this! So let's get to it!

WHAT IS LABOR MANAGEMENT?

The term *labor management* refers to all aspects of managing labor, including labor productivity, use of premium labor such as contract labor and overtime, and skill mix which refers to how higher and lower paid skill sets are coupled together to get the most value. We will cover all of these topics in this chapter. Let's start with the BIG one . . .productivity.

WHAT IS PRODUCTIVITY?

Productivity is a measure of resource utilization or efficiency. Efficiency measures how much XX (resource) is required to produce YY (an output). XX can be money, time, gasoline, or any kind of resource. YY can be any kind of output: a car, surgery, a number of miles.

Productivity is not unique to hospitals, or even to healthcare. In this era of competitive economics, practically everyone it seems is measuring how much better, quicker, and cheaper they (or their product) can do something than everyone else. Car companies tell us how many more miles per gallon their car will give us compared to the competition. The grocery store tells us the cost of Brand A's product per ounce compared to Brand B. Websites tell us the price of a ticket to fly 500 miles on one airline compared to another. It's all about who can be the most efficient. Why? Because whoever can be the most efficient will have the lowest cost (quality, etc. being held constant). And whoever has the lowest cost can either lower their price to attract more customers or keep prices the same as the competition and make more money. In healthcare, we probably try to do a little of both. If we have lower cost, we can accept more of a discount from the insurers (which may attract more patients), or we can be paid the same as everyone else and make more money. By now you certainly remember that the money is really just about what it can do for you—not the amount of it you have.

Labor productivity in hospitals is the number of hours ("man hours") it takes to complete a task. The task can be one day of patient care, one registration, preparing one patient meal, performing one minute of surgery, delivering one baby.

Depending on the sophistication of your hospital's information technology system, labor productivity reporting may be a daily task for you. On the other hand, you may not have information available until after the end of a pay period. Some department heads and supervisors may see productivity data only after month end.

For purposes of this book, I am going assume that you receive this information daily. The concepts are always the same, but daily information is best because it gives frequent opportunities to make adjustments and to positively impact your month before it's over.

WHY DOES LABOR PRODUCTIVITY MATTER IN HOSPITALS?

By now you've heard me point out a number of times that labor is the single largest operating expense a hospital has and that it usually consumes around

50% of total expenses. I've also indicated strongly that management or non-management of labor expenses can make the difference between a hospital making a healthy margin and going broke.

Before we get into how you can better manage your department, let's look at a quick illustration of what the impact of labor management can be.

We've talked previously about each department having it's own statistic to measure and compare with, right? Well, when you want to measure and compare labor for the whole hospital, you typically use Adjusted Patient Days (APDs). You remember from **Chapter 1** that an APD is a volume indicator that adjusts to consider both inpatient days and equivalent outpatient "days" (see **Chapter 1** for more details if needed). So when you want to measure productivity for the whole hospital, the industry standard is *Man Hours per Adjusted Patient Day* or MH/APD.

Let's say that the budget for your hospital is 25.50 paid MH/APD. That means that each day, for each APD your hospital has, there are to be 25.50 hours paid to provide that care. Remember, this covers the entire hospital, so it includes everything from Admitting and Administration to Housekeeping and Facilities—and everything in between (including Nursing and all of the ancillary services).

What is the cost to the hospital if instead of running at 25.50 MH/APD, the hospital incurs 26.00 MH/APD? Thirty extra minutes per patient per day. So if Nursing, Pharmacy, Lab, Radiology and Anesthesia, each spent a measly five extra minutes per day with each patient, it would add up to *an extra 30 minutes per patient, per day.* Can't be that much—or can it? Let's see.

Assume an average census of 500
Assume an adjustment factor of 1.80
Then over a year, APDs are 500 x 365 x 1.80 = 328,500
Assume an overall Average Hourly Rate (AHR) of $32.00/hr
At the budgeted 25.50 MH/APD, the labor cost is:
25.50 x 328,500 x $32 = $268,056,000

But what happens if you add those five little minutes each for six departments? If the hospital actual runs at 26.00 MH/APD instead of 25.50, the labor cost is:

26.00 x 328,500 x $32 = $273,312,000

The difference? A whopping $5,256,000! Wow! Think of all the things you could do with an extra $5 million! Now you see why it is so important—and even small differences can add up to a lot of money.

So let's move on to talking about how you can help your hospital have a healthy margin—instead of going broke!

If you are reading this book in sequence, then you've already read the chapter on budgeting labor. If you haven't actually read it yet, you may want to. I'll assume you have, so we'll only do a very quick recap here to set the stage.

Every department has some combination of fixed and variable labor. However, for productivity monitoring purposes, most hospitals treat departments as either being Fixed, or Variable. Fixed means that the number of FTEs in the department stay the same, regardless of the volume in the hospital. Typical fixed departments are administration, facilities, medical records, etc. Most departments that generate revenue are considered to be variable. A variable department is one whose staffing levels move with hospital volume. Examples of variable departments are Nursing, Lab, X-ray, Pharmacy, etc.

THE BASIC MATH BEHIND HOSPITAL PRODUCTIVITY

Before I figured out I wanted to be an accountant, I thought I wanted to be a high school math teacher, because I always liked numbers. And I have found over the years that there is actually a lot of math in the accounting world. Hospital productivity is one example.

Productivity is a mathematical ratio. For hospitals, the numerator is *always* "man hours." They can be worked, paid, productive, non-productive—whatever you want. But they will *always* be man hours.

The denominator for hospitals is always a statistic. It can be (and most times is) different for each department, but it is always a statistic. The statistic is almost always a volume indicator. More generically, it is always a *size* indicator. The reason I say that is because for housekeeping and facilities, the department statistic is usually square feet of the hospital. For most departments, however, the statistic indicates the volume of tasks done. It changes every day. For housekeeping and facilities, the square footage is an adequate indicator of the volume of their workload because it is assumed that they clean/care for the entire facility every day—so the statistic does not change.

For productivity, a smaller number is better. That means you are more efficient.

Since it is a ratio, there are two mathematical ways to make it smaller:

1. Decrease the numerator (man hours), while holding the denominator steady. This would mean using fewer man hours to complete the same number of tasks.

2. Increase the denominator (statistic) while holding the numerator steady. This would mean using the same number of man hours to perform more tasks.

The reverse is also true.

3. If you increase the numerator while holding the denominator steady, the ratio will go up. This means you used more man hours to complete the same number of tasks—which means you were less efficient.

4. If you decrease the denominator while holding the numerator steady, the ratio will increase. This means the same number of people accomplished fewer tasks.

So when you want to analyze your productivity compared to budget, or compared to a prior period, if today's actual productivity number is *smaller* than whatever you are comparing it to, then either item #1 or item# 2 must be true (or both). If today's number is *bigger*, then either items #3 or #4 must be true (or both).

I know this may seem very basic, but it will be important for the variable departments when we discuss how you can improve your own department's productivity.

THE NUMERATOR: MAN HOURS

First let's talk about the numerator: **Man Hours** (MH). Man hours is the total number of hours used over a period of time to complete a task, or multiples of the same task. Perhaps a simpler way to say it, is that it is the total number of hours charged to, or accumulated in your department over a period of time. That's not as generic of a description, but perhaps it is one you can relate to better? Your data source will likely be your payroll system. When you are adding up the hours, you can add *all* hours, or subsets of hours. Perhaps you want to look at only worked hours (and exclude time off), or look at just non-productive hours, which will include time off and time spent in orientation training, or at a seminars, etc., time you pay people for that is not time spent "completing the task" (see **Chapter 1** for clarification). Your payroll department can probably provide you with codes you can use to sort out only the types of hours you want to measure. The best productivity reports will show you both actual worked and paid hours, and budgeted worked and paid hours. That will simplify where you need to start to analyze your variances.

The assumption until now is that the hours in the payroll system are correct. Of course, that's a very big assumption. Depending on the discipline of your hospital, managers often do not verify the accuracy of payroll until the pay period ends. If your hospital reports productivity on a basis that is more frequent that the pay periods (such as daily or weekly), then this discipline is critical to having accurate productivity numbers. Let's walk through an example.

Let's say you are the Director of a department that is budgeted to have ten FTEs. You actually have 11. One of them is on vacation, so obviously that employee does not clock-in. If you do not go into the payroll system and enter those hours, then each day that week, the payroll system may only show 10 FTEs. Administration will review your productivity report and think everything is fine. Then, at the end of the pay period, you enter the 40 hours of PTO taken.

Oops! All of a sudden, you are back to 11 FTEs. And Administration is probably not happy. As a CFO, I can tell you that I place a lot of reliance on the report, and use it to project labor costs for the month. If it is incomplete, I will underestimate my costs.

THE DENOMINATOR: STATISTICS

Now let's talk about the denominator—**the statistic.** In **Chapter** 7 we discussed statistics from the perspective of setting them for the budget. But we didn't talk about how they are captured or counted during the day each day. Where does the statistic come from? There may be as many answers to that question as there are hospitals, and hospital departments.

Some department statistics are simple, such as the square footage statistic used by facilities and housekeeping. Some departmental statistics are straightforward, an example of which is patient days, which are captured automatically at midnight. But many departments require manual input to capture statistical information. Depending on your hospital, the statistic may be reported manually in a department log, or, more likely, it is captured when someone manually inputs (or scans) departmental charges into the department's charge system. Surgery is one common example of a department that may be based on a log dependent upon charges input into the computer system. ED is another. If you don't already know how your department charges are captured, you will definitely want to find out. I prefer the *'charges in the system'* approach because it leaves nothing to interpretation. If the charge is in the system, the statistic exists; if there is no charge, there is no statistic.

Think about that for a moment: if there is no charge, there is no statistic. Add that to the mathematical fact #2 above that says *productivity gets better when the denominator (the statistic) increases.* This means that you can help your productivity by simply making sure you enter your department's charges in a timely fashion—every day. This is just one of many reasons that having charges in timely is important.

For some departments, there are also many obstacles that can delay charges being captured on time. One simple example is that in the ED, charges vary depending on the "level of care" given to the patient. The level cannot be assigned until all documentation is recorded on the chart. Sometimes physicians and nurses get busy and don't stop to complete the chart. Or they think it is complete, but when it gets to Medical Records, missing information is detected and the chart is returned to the department to be completed. Another simple example comes from Surgery. Maybe a new supply item was used during a procedure. Charging the entire procedure may be halted while the new item is added to the CDM (see **Chapter 2**).

If you are not already familiar with how charge capture works in your department, you will want to find out. You should also work to ensure charges are captured as quickly as possible so that your productivity is accurate. No sense having an unfavorable productivity statistic just because charges are missing!

For most departments, "a stat is a stat is a stat." One baby delivered is assumed to utilize (on average) the same resources as another baby delivered.

But for departments that do many different tasks, this is not true. An MRI scan of the brain utilizes much more resources than an MRI scan of an elbow. So the resources used by the department on a day when 20 brain scans were performed is much higher than a day when they performed 20 elbows. How can we level that playing field?

We use *Relative Value Units* (RVU). Remember in **Chapter 2** when we discussed how DRGs have "case weights" that indicate the resources used to care for the patient, and a DRG with a weight of 1.5 was assumed to use 1.5 times the resources as a DRG with a weight of 1? RVUs do the same thing.

Let's look again at our MRI example. If procedure A is deemed to use twice the resources as procedure B, then procedure A will be "assigned" two RVUs, while procedure B is assigned one RVU. That means that if the department performed one procedure A and one procedure B on the same day, at the end of the day the stat for the day will be *three*. A few of the departments that commonly utilize RVUs are Lab, Imaging, Pharmacy, and Therapies (PT, OT, and Speech).

Now we've set the stage to understand how productivity is computed, so let's move on to understanding the reports when you look at them.

We've learned that smaller is better, right? So when you look at your numbers compared to budget, less than budget is good, greater than budget is *not so good*. If the number is less, as long as you feel comfortable that the numerator and denominator are correct, you can probably scratch this off your to-do list for today and move on to the next thing. That's always good, right? So let's help you understand how to analyze your numbers if they *aren't* less than budget so you can figure out what changes you need to make to get things back on track. Allowing you to move on to tasks that you find more valuable.

How you analyze your variances depends on whether your department productivity is managed on a fixed or variable basis.

Since they are simpler, let's start with fixed. Even if your department is not fixed, I highly recommend reading this section, anyway. Many of the concepts discussed here can also apply to variable departments.

FIXED DEPARTMENTS

If a department is considered fixed, labor productivity management is very simple and straightforward: how many FTEs do you have compared to budget? Less or more? If the answer is "less," there probably won't be any more questions (from a productivity point of view anyway). If the answer is "more," you need to be able to explain why.

Don't panic. You know the answers. Well, *maybe* you know the answers. But maybe it will take a little research. You're a good manager. You didn't just let extra people work for no reason (did you?). So let's explore some possible reasons that your productivity report might show you as having too many staff.

Possibility #1: The Budget is Wrong

I hate to admit this, but it is possible. (Don't ever assume we never make mistakes in finance!) Depending on who did it, how your budget is done, and whether or not you got to see it before it was finalized, it may be possible that the budget is wrong. Maybe you were supposed to have 10 FTEs, and a keystroke error gave you one instead. If the budget is wrong, how many FTEs should you have been budgeted, and how does your current staffing compare to that? If it's less, then you are done. Advance to go and collect $200!

Possibility #2: The Final Actual Budget is Correct But Different than the Requested Budget

It is also possible that the budget you requested is different than the final budget. This can happen if management "trims" your budget and forgets to tell you. I know it sounds like something that would only happen in a poorly run finance department, but believe me, it can happen very easily. Things can get very crazy at the end of the budget preparation, and last-minute changes are being made all over the place. It can be hard even to remember what all was changed in those final days or hours.

If this happens to you, my recommendation would be to stay calm when you meet with management to discuss it. They may have made other decisions you don't know about, decisions that make the changes to your budget make total sense. Let me give you just one example: if your hospital is part of a large system with a central office, then perhaps some of the tasks you currently perform will be moved to the central office, so you will need less staff. I realize, of course, that if that is the reason, then a whole different can of worms is now open. But those are outside the scope of this book. I just wanted to show you there are many possible valid reasons. The one thing I would hope is true, is that there IS a reason. Now, if you requested more staff than you currently have, with no reason for the increase, then don't be surprised that management "trimmed" your budget! But DO go talk to them—before you get too upset or stressed out.

Possibility #3: Your Staffing Model has Changed

Refer back to **Exhibit 9** in **Chapter 8** *(page 74)*. If your **Exhibit 9** matches the budget, but your current staffing does not, then compare your current staffing model to the one shown in **Exhibit 9**. Obviously something is different. Have you changed something about how you staff the department since you did your budget? If so, then what and why? Perhaps it is something management agreed to. If so—*great!* You're done! If not, then perhaps you need to talk with Administration about what changes you made and why. They may either agree or request you reduce something somewhere to get back to your budgeted FTEs. If you do have more staff, one possible defense is that the cost is the same. Perhaps you replaced a pharmacist with two pharmacy techs—two bodies instead of one, but each tech cost less than half the cost of a pharmacist, so the labor cost is actually less. (they will *like* that answer!) If the staffing model hasn't changed, but for some reason you used more FTEs, then you'll need to keep going to figure it out.

Possibility #4: Non-Productive Time is Over Budget

The next possible reason you may have more paid FTEs than were budgeted is that although productive time (the worked hours) were on budget, non-productive hours were over budget. Remember Total paid hours include both productive and non-productive time. Get a breakdown of the two and compare that to the productive and non-productive budgets. If the productive hours are ok, but the non-productive hours are over budget, then Possibility #4 is your answer. So let's assume you have determined that it is your non-productive hours being over budget that has caused your variance. How non-productive time runs over budget in your department depends on how your hospital accounts for non-productive time. There are two Options:

1. Non-productive time is only charged to you as it is accrued, but not when it is taken.

2. Non-productive time is charged to you when it is accrued, AND when it is taken. If this is your hospital's policy, then an offsetting credit is taken in some other (obscure) department to eliminate the double counting of the expense.

Let's inspect Option #1 first. Think about your own paycheck—your check stub probably shows the number of hours you were paid for either working or for paid leave of some kind (vacation, sick time etc.), and it also shows the number of hours of time off you earned during this pay period. It probably also shows how many hours of unused time off you have left. Chances are, your hospital has a policy of paying you for those unused hours if you quit before you use them. Let's say that for exempt staff, your hospital policy is 26 paid days off per year—ten vacation days, eight sick days, and eight holidays. That is 26 days x 8 hours per day = 208 hours.

208 hours happens to be 10% of 2080, by the way, which is why 10% non-productive time is such a common percentage used when budgeting. Anyway, back to our story. 208 hours over the course of a year computes to 4 hours per week (208/52).

Since the hospital owes you for that time until you take it off, it must record the liability. The way to record a liability is to record an expense. So each week, even though you *worked* 40 hours, because you also earned four hours of time off that needs to be recorded as a liability, the hospital will actually *charge* your department for 44 hours of time on your account: 40 hours *worked* and four

EXHIBIT 19												
Accounting for Non-Productive Time												
	Payperiod											
	1	2	3	4	5	6	7	8	9	10	11	Total
What Actually Happened:												
Hours worked	40	40	40	40	40	40	40	40	40	40	-	400
Time off earned	4	4	4	4	4	4	4	4	4	4	4	44
Time off taken	-	-	-	-	-	-	-	-	-	-	40	40
Total Time	44	44	44	44	44	44	44	44	44	44	44	484
Time Charged to Dept:												
Possibility #1	44	44	44	44	44	44	44	44	44	44	4	444
Possibility #2	44	44	44	44	44	44	44	44	44	44	44	484
Time Charged Elsewhere:												
Possibility #1	-	-	-	-	-	-	-	-	-	-	-	-
Possibility #2	-	-	-	-	-	-	-	-	-	-	(40)	(40)
Total Time Charged:												
Possibility #1	44	44	44	44	44	44	44	44	44	44	4	444
Possibility #2	44	44	44	44	44	44	44	44	44	44	4	444
Option # 1: time worked + time accrued = charge to Dept. (time taken not charged to dept)												
Time Charged to Dept	44	44	44	44	44	44	44	44	44	44	44	484
Time Reversed out of Dept	-	-	-	-	-	-	-	-	-	-	(40)	(40)
Time Reversed Elsewhere	-	-	-	-	-	-	-	-	-	-	-	-
Total Time Charged	44	44	44	44	44	44	44	44	44	44	4	444
Option #2: time worked + time accrued + time taken ALL charged to dept												
Time Charged to Dept	44	44	44	44	44	44	44	44	44	44	44	484
Time Reversed out of Dept	-	-	-	-	-	-	-	-	-	-	-	-
Time Reversed Elsewhere	-	-	-	-	-	-	-	-	-	-	(40)	(40)
Total Time Charged	44	44	44	44	44	44	44	44	44	44	4	444

non-productive hours. I know this may seem confusing. Go back and re-read if you need to.

OK. So now it's ten weeks later, and you have earned a total of 40 hours of time off. You decide to take a week of vacation. If your hospital falls into Option #1, then the time off is not charged to your department (well, it is, but it is reversed out, so the net effect is no charge. Don't worry we'll illustrate later). Your department was already charged for those hours as you *earned* them. But when you *take* them, the hospital charges that time "against" the liability it had accrued. Doing that reduces the liability they have to you. This is appropriate because now if you quit, the hospital does not owe you those 40 hours anymore, so they can reduce their liability.

Maybe walking through an example will help. I know this topic is sounding more like accounting than you wanted, isn't it? But at the same time, hopefully you agree it is useful to know and understand.

Look at **Exhibit 19**. Here we pretend for illustrative purposes that you are a one-man department. At the top of the exhibit, we illustrate what actually occurred. For now, focus on the section that refers to "Option #1." This example shows how the accounting works over an 11-week period. During weeks one through ten, you worked 40 hours and accrued four more hours of ETO. So for hospital accounting purposes, they paid you for 40 hours and recorded a liability of four additional hours each week. Thus, if you saw your department financial statements for each of those weeks, you would see an expense of 44 hours recorded. So through week ten, the department had been charged 440 hours: 400 worked, plus 40 more accrued. Then in week 11, you take the 40 hours you have accrued off. The payroll system does not know whether you worked or were on vacation—it just knows that you were paid. So it charges the 40 hours to your department. However, accounting knows the department has already incurred that expense, so it reverses the time out and reduces the hospital's liability to you for 'time earned but not taken.' So after 11 weeks, you have been paid for 400 hours of worked time, plus 40 hours of vacation time off, and the hospital still owes you four hours if you quit. A total of 444 hours. And your department financials year to date are correct, showing the 444 hours.

Now let's examine Option #2: it's been awhile, so let me repeat it. Option #2 is that:

Non-productive time is charged to you when it is accrued, and when it is taken. If this is your hospital's policy, then an offsetting credit is taken in some other (obscure) department to eliminate the double counting of the expense.

Look again now at **Exhibit 19**. But this time focus on the section that refers to Option #2. Everything is the same as Option #1 during weeks one through ten. Then, week 11 is different. Since you were still paid for the 40 hours you took off, the payroll system charges your paycheck to your department. What is different in week 11 is that the reversal of the hours to reduce the hospital liability is not done in your department. It is done somewhere else. So now, after 11 weeks, your department hours are overstated. The hospital's total hours are correct. It's just your individual department that is incorrect.

"How unfair!" you exclaim. Why would anyone do it that way? For most hospitals, Option #2 is how it is done. Option #1 is very cumbersome and requires extensive manual calculations. I'm not saying that makes it right. Just saying that's how it is.

Whew! That was a little bit intense, huh? Too much accounting? I apologize, but I also know I am frequently asked to explain this to people. If you are held accountable for productivity in your department, you will need to know which option your hospital uses. Because it will determine how you examine variances in non-productive time. Oh yes—that's what we were talking about when we got sidetracked isn't it? So let's get back to that then.

To do that, let's go back for a moment to our budget-building. Look at the hours section (at the top) of **Exhibit 9** *(page 74)* for the month of *January*. Look at the total Paid hours—740. Now look at Total Worked hours—673. That means that Budgeted non-productive time was 740 - 673 = 67 hours. The magical 10%. So if your non-productive hours are greater than 67, you need to figure out why. Now maybe you see why I needed to explain Options#1 and #2 to you? To know how to tackle this question, you need to know which one your hospital uses.

If your hospital uses Option #1, then you are only being charged for accrued time. And if you are over budget, then that means you are accruing at a higher percentage than was budgeted. What could cause that to happen?

Let's go back to our one-person department example.

Let's say you have worked at the hospital for four years. With four years of tenure, you accrue 26 days of ETO (which we know is 26 x 8hrs/day = 208 hours = 10% of your annual hours of 2,080). But company policy provides for you to increase your ETO accrual starting on your fifth anniversary of employment to an extra week of time off (40 more hours) each year. So now you get 208 + 40 = 248 hours = 12% of the same 2,080 hours per year. If the budget was based on last year's historical percentage, then you will be off every month starting when your five-year anniversary passes. Imagine how complicated things get when you have a very large department with people coming and going. Some have low ETO accruals, and others have been employed a long time and have high accrual percentages. In fact, the number may move every month. The other possibility is that the hospital changed its ETO accrual policy and forgot to adjust the budget. Remember the golden rule of budgeting? "Prior year results +/- current year changes = next year's budget."

Here is yet another example of one of the many things to think about in terms of changes that should be considered in order to have a good budget. Well, at least you know the answer as to why you are over budget.

If your hospital uses Option #2, then you are being charged for accrued time and time taken. So everything we just talked about with Option #1 applies, *plus* there are now other issues that will add to them.

Let's go back to **Exhibit 9**. Even if you managed the department exactly as shown on the schedule, and if the 10% is adequate for accrued time off—you will still always—I repeat, always—be over budget every time even one person takes time off. Remember, the hospital has an offsetting credit somewhere else to cover this, so the hospital as a whole is not over budget. Just you!

But let's take it a step further. Let's assume that the budget was prepared using the prior year percentages, and (for discussion purposes) let's set aside the fact that the accrual percentage will likely change over time. Let's pretend you had perfect information to budget for accrued time. So the only variable is budgeting the time actually taken. Now there's a dart on the wall! Yes, you can usually do a decent job of knowing that holidays and summer vacations will spike time off in certain months, but you can never know when someone will have unexpected FMLA or get sick. Maybe, over the course of a year, the highs and lows will even out, but in any one month, these hours can fluctuate wildly.

Chances are, your hospital uses Option #2, in which case the only thing you can do is to know what happened if non-productive time is over budget. Other than being responsible about not allowing too many folks to go out on vacation at one time, no one expects you to manage this. That's the good news. And now that you understand it all, I'll tell you that this is why most hospitals only hold their department managers accountable for Productive time.

Possibility #5: Extenuating Circumstances

Sometimes things happen that are just simply beyond your control. There are many situations that may apply here. I'll give a few examples to illustrate:

1. For a fixed department, large volume fluctuations would be considered extenuating circumstances. If your department normally runs on a fixed schedule every day, but because of a large increase in volume you need to have extra people work; that is an extenuating circumstance for you (a volume fluctuation would *not* be an extenuating circumstance for a productivity variance in a variable department because their productivity measure is a "per unit of service" indicator, whereas a fixed department is based strictly on a fixed number of FTEs).

2. Mandatory training or meetings that are unplanned or unbudgeted for all staff. Maybe you need to have staff attend training after their shift to learn a new software program. If you have a large department, even a two-hour session can add up in hours—and money, too, if it generates overtime.

3. Some type of disaster incident occurs at the hospital, and your staff is involved in managing it. Or perhaps there is a disaster drill that your staff participates in. This takes them away from their duties, and they have to work extra to get caught up.

You get the idea. The important thing is to know what are things beyond your ability to manage around, and things you *should* be able to manage around. For example, although the meetings described in #2 above are an extenuating circumstance, regular meetings with your staff to keep them informed is not an extenuating circumstance. Those meetings are controlled by you. All of the examples above are situations where outside circumstances resulted in a need for you to have your staff work extra hours.

Possibility #6: You Blew It

If none of the other possibilities provide an answer as to why you used more staff than you were budgeted for, the only remaining possibility is that you blew it, because if none of the other possibilities explained things, then that means that:

- the budget was exactly what you requested

- you have not changed your staffing schedule

- the variance is not caused by non-productive hours being over budget

- there were no extenuating circumstances

If none of the four statements above are true, then you weren't paying attention, and people worked who were not supposed to work—or they came in earlier and/or stayed later. *This* is why management focuses on productivity.

Remember the story about 30 minutes a day costing over $5 million a year? People hanging around talking to friends and not clocking out adds up. The 30 minutes a day story used a 2% variance. Think about that—just 2%. So if your employees are supposed to work 40 hours a week, then .8 hours per week is 2% over a year's time. But wait. The time will be paid as overtime (time and a half). So the hard truth is that it takes only .5 hours per week to increase labor costs 2%. I read somewhere years ago that employees who are sloppy punching out typically adds 1-2% to labor costs. Something else to think about, yes?

It's pretty clear, you can make a huge difference by managing your department, no matter how small it might be.

If your labor overage is caused by Possibilities #1-5, then a simple talk with management will usually take care of things. But if it is caused by Possibility # 6, you will need to begin taking a tougher stand with your employees about time management. Sometimes you need only to "mandate" that no time is to be worked in excess of the time scheduled. Tell folks they are responsible for managing their time. If they need to stay late one day, they need to let you know so you can schedule them out early later in the week. Make them accountable. When you review/sign-off payroll and see employees with overtime, call them in and ask them why. And remind them it cannot continue. Another common way in which time can get away from a new leader is employees who "skip" lunch. Most hospital's payroll systems assume a lunch break. Employees then tell their manager when they did not take one because things were too hectic etc. But be careful. Again, remember the $5 million cost of an extra 30 minutes a day. If you aren't watching, employees can easily add 2.50 hours per week—at overtime rates, by punching in and out as scheduled but by skipping lunch.

MANAGED AS FIXED—MONITORED AS VARIABLE

If you have a department in which this phenomenon applies, you know exactly what I'm talking about.

You have a department in which the industry standard is a variable MH/ Stat. But for your hospital, the service your department offers (for whatever reason) does not have very high volume. Speech therapy can sometimes be a good example of this. Depending on your hospital's specialties, this department may or may not be busy. But it is needed.

So even if it isn't very busy, you still must maintain a small staff. You can't send them home every time volume drops, then ask them to drop everything and come in when you have volume. And you don't really know when that will be. No one would ever work for you if that was how their schedule worked. So you set a schedule based on your experience of how and when volumes tend to occur. If volume is over budget, you probably have extra capacity to absorb it without adding any hours, so your numbers look good. Make sense?

Remember, when we're talking about productivity, *smaller is better*—and in this situation, if you do not add hours to the numerator but the denominator (volume) increases, then the ratio will shrink. Shrinking productivity ratios are good! However, the opposite is also true. What if volume drops? Then the numerator stays the same and the denominator drops, making the ratio bigger. Not good. Let's walk through an example:

Exhibit 20 illustrates this phenomenon. Notice the budget provides 520 worked hours per month (three FTEs). And in both months 1 and 2, you came in exactly on budget with 520 worked hours *(row 1, columns B and E)*. The budget also assumed 1,000 units of service per month *(row 2, columns A and D)*. For a Speech Therapy department, the unit of service is probably based on how the services are billed. If your hospital bills in 15-minute increments, then 1 fifteen-minute increment is probably your statistic. Now look at the actual volume in Month 1 *(row 2, column B)*. It came in higher than budget *(row 2, column A)*. But because you probably operate under a fixed staffing model, regardless of volume, when the added volume occurred, it just meant that the same number of people were simply busier. No one needed to work more hours to provide the extra services. You performed a higher volume of work with the same resources, which made the department more productive; resulting in a

Row/Col		A	B	C	D	E	F

		EXHIBIT 20					
		Productivity Comparison					
		Speech Therapy Department					
Row/Col		A	B	C	D	E	F
		Month 1			Month 2		
		Budget	Actual	Variance	Budget	Actual	Variance
1	Worked Man Hours	520	520	0	520	520	0
2	Units of Service	1,000	1,200	200	1,000	800	(200)
3	Worked MH/Stat	0.52	0.43	(0.09)	0.52	0.65	0.13

lower productivity ratio. In Month 2, just the opposite was true. Your staffing model is the same, fixed at three FTEs. But when volume drops, you can't send people home. So your hours are the same, even though your volume is less. You performed less work with the same number of man hours, which—this made you less productive, giving you a *higher* (worse) productivity ratio.

If you are responsible for a department like this, chances are good that management understands. In a hospital department with larger volume, the department is expected to run as a variable department and flex staffing up or down for volume. But when volumes are low, the department must maintain at least a core level of fixed staff. So when you are reviewing your productivity, follow the steps outlined above in the previous (Fixed Department) section. The key is to know at what volume levels you "become" a Fixed Staffing department. Make sure you and management agree on that! You may well have differing opinions. Perhaps you feel core staffing is five FTEs. Perhaps management thinks core staffing is three FTEs. Just make sure you are both on the same page. If you disagree, you may need to demonstrate why you feel five FTEs is core.

Do you keep a log of your patient volumes? If not, you may be able to have finance get you a report showing your volumes by hour of the day. You may be able to show that volume comes in spurts, so that during certain times of the day you need more than one person, but other times, volume is very low, and your staff is basically here "in case" they are needed.

VARIABLE DEPARTMENTS (INCLUDING NURSING) AND COST PER UNIT OF SERVICE

If you are in charge of a department that is held accountable for productivity as being 100% variable, then this may be the most complicated part of this book for you.

I promise we will go slowly. Feel free to move through this at your own speed, and go back over it as many times as you need to. We will also cover the concepts of Cost per Unit of Service in this section, so even if you run a fixed department, you will still want to read this section.

OK, did you take a very deep breath? Are you ready? Let's do it!

There is a lot to cover here, so I am not going to repeat the lesson content covered in **Chapter 8** on budgeting labor. Feel free to flip back and refresh your memory if you need to.

Chapter 8 covered *how* a staffing matrix is translated into a budget. So for purposes of this chapter, I am going to assume you understand how the budget numbers were derived, and that you agree with them (i.e., that you do not feel the budget is incorrect). I am also going to assume that the staffing matrix in place when the budget was prepared is still in use today.

These two assumptions relate to Possibilities 1 through 3 above (covering

Fixed Department variance explanations). Please *do* speak with your superior if you *do* think the budget is incorrect, or the staffing matrix has changed. But this material is complicated enough without adding these complications.

So if possibilities 1 through 3 outlined above do not apply to you, then where do you start to unravel the reasons you are off on your productivity numbers? And how far off are you? Does the variance translate into a material financial impact?

Let's look at **Exhibit 21** *(page 142)*. This exhibit shows the detailed calculations for a Nursing unit. Before we start working with it, take a minute to familiarize yourself with the format and contents. Don't worry about understanding it—we will walk through it. But notice:

a. The rows are numbered along the left side under the column titled "Line." I will use these line numbers to reference parts of the exhibit.

b. There is a column labeled "formula." Each row either has a formula or contains the word "input." If the data is from an external source (i.e. is NOT a formula), then you see the word "input." If the cell value is calculated from other numbers within the exhibit, then this column contains the formula. For example, the line 5 "Total Paid hours" formula says "line 3 + line 4." This means that the values across line 5 are always the sum of the respective line 3 and line 4 above it; e.g., under the April "actual" column, line 3 is 10,498 + line 4 is 839, so line 5 is the sum: 10,498 + 839 =11,337.

c. Notice that each month has 3 columns: a column titled "Actual;" a column titled "Budget;" and a column titled "More/(Less)." The formula for this column is: Actual minus Budget. Sometimes more is better (for example when actual volume is more than budget, that would be good). But remember, with productivity ratios, less is better and more is worse.

Now that you are a little bit familiar with the exhibit, let's step back and see what is says. Remember at the beginning of the book I talked about finance simply telling a story? That you just needed to know the language to unlock the story? Here is an example of that.

Your productivity report probably does not have all of this information on it, but this information is always behind whatever numbers you are provided. Your report may simply have Actual and Budgeted FTEs *(line 9)* and Actual and Budgeted Paid MH/Stat *(line 12)*. But when you have a variance, you need to know all of the rest of this information to be able to understand the story. So let's take a closer look!

Let's pretend your productivity report just came out for the month of April. As illustrated in **Exhibit 21**, it shows your Paid MH/Stat came in at 10.50 on a budget of 9.79, so you are off by .71 MH/Stat *(see line 12)*. Hospital policy is that you must respond in writing whenever you have a "material" variance. What to do? Where to start?

	EXHIBIT 21				
	Nursing Unit A				
	Productivity Report				
	Department Stat		Patient Days + Equivalent Observation Days		
Line	Description	Formula	April 2010		
			Actual	Budget	More/(Less)
1	Total UOS	Input	1,080	1,200	(120)
2	ADC	line 1 / days in month	36	40	(4)
3	Total Worked Hours	Input	10,498	10,680	(182)
4	Total non-Prod Hours	Input	839	1,068	(229)
5	Total Paid Hours	line 3 + line 4	11,337	11,748	(412)
6	Hours per FTE	2,080/365 x # days in month	170.96	170.96	-
7	Worked FTEs	line 3 / line 6	61.40	62.47	(1.07)
8	Non-Prod FTEs	line 4 / line 6	4.91	6.25	(1.34)
9	Total Paid FTEs	line 5 / line 6	66.31	68.72	(2.41)
10	Worked MH/Stat	line 3 / line 1	9.72	8.90	0.82
11	Non-Prod MH/Stat	line 4 / line 1	0.78	0.89	(0.11)
12	Total Paid MH/Stat	line 5 / line 1	10.50	9.79	0.71
13	Average Hourly Rate	line 16 / line 5	$31.50	$31.01	$0.49
14	Cost of Worked FTEs	Input	$330,674	$331,187	$(512)
15	Cost of Non-Prod FTEs	Input	$26,422	$33,119	$(6,696)
16	Total Cost of FTEs	Input	$357,128	$364,305	$(7,177)
17	Worked Cost per UOS	line 14 / line 1	$306.18	$275.99	$30.19
18	Non-Prod Cost per UOS	line 15 / line 1	$24.47	$27.60	$(3.13)
19	Total Cost per UOS	line 16 / line 1	$330.67	$303.59	$27.09
20	$$ Impact of Volume Variance	line 1 more/(less) column x line 19 budget column			$(36,431)
21	$$ Impact of MH/Stat Variance	line 12 more/(less) column x line 1 actual x line 13 budget			$23,698
22	$$ Impact of AHR Variance	line 13 more/(less) column x line 5 actual column			$5,555
23	Total Variance				$(7,177)
24	Overtime Hours	Input	367	-	367
25	Total Worked Hours	From line 3 above	10,498	10,680	(182)
26	Overtime %	line 24 / line 25	3.5%	0.0%	3.5%
27	AHR excluding OT	line 16 / [(line 5 - line 24) + (1.5 x line 24)]	31.00	31.01	(0.01)
28	Impact of OT on AHR	line 13 - line 27	0.50	-	0.50

First, do you have a material variance? Is .71 MH/Stat over budget "material?" It may seem very small to you. But remember that .5 MH/stat can cost a hospital $5 million a year. The smaller the department statistic, the smaller the variance needs to be for it to add up to a lot of money.

For example, a pharmacy that uses doses as a department stat may release several hundred thousand doses in a single month. So even if the MH/stat was only over by .01, that .01 is 2,000 hours (more than 11 FTEs) when applied to a monthly statistic of 200,000 doses. Your COO or CFO may define "material" for you. For me, the variance is "material" if it is more than 5% unfavorable to the budget. Since your budget was 9.79MH/Stat, 5% is (9.79 x .05 =) .49. Any variance more than .49 unfavorable is material (using my formula), so yes, at .71, your variance is material, and needs to be investigated.

But you know you manage your department very tightly. How can this be? Why do these numbers imply that you don't? Is that what they say?

Before we look specifically for the answer, let's see what the numbers *behind* the productivity numbers tell us. What is the real story?

Starting at the top on lines 1 and 2, we see that volume (UOS and ADC) was less than budget. We also see on lines 3,4,5 and 7,8,9 that worked, non-productive, and total hours are all under budget, too. Line 14,15 and 16 also show that salary costs are all under budget.

So why does line 12 on this report show you were over budget? How could that be? And as long as you are under budget in terms of salary dollars spent, why does it matter?

Let's answer the second question first. The reason it matters goes back to lines 1 and 2, showing that volumes were less than budget. Remember that *volumes drive revenue*. So if volumes were under budget, then revenue was probably under budget, too. If revenue was under budget, then there is less money to spend on salaries. So salaries *need* to be under budget.

How far under budget do they need to be? Aha! Is it starting to come together now?

The answer to that question brings us back to the productivity report and why it matters. For a *variable* department, since revenue is tied to volume, salaries need to tie to volume, as well.

Did yours? Now we move back to the question above about how could productivity be over budget when salaries were under budget? It is because your paid hours were not under budget as much as volume was under budget. Let me say that again in a different way:

Productivity is over budget because your volume variance is greater than your hours variance: hours did not move as much as volume did.

This is the "curse" of being measured as being 100% variable. Remember, we discussed that no department is ever 100% variable. It is impossible to simply move hours with every ebb and flow of volume. Let's keep going and see what other facts we can gather in our story.

Lines 10 and 11 show the breakout of Paid MH/Stat between worked and non-productive, commonly referred to as "non-prod". We see here that the problem is on the *worked* side. Non-prod MH/Stat is actually under budget. On the worked side, the budget was 8.90 and you came in at 9.72; an overage of .82 MH/Stat. But since the non-prod MH/Stat was *under* by .11, the overall Paid MH/Stat (line 12) was only over by the net of the .82 unfavorable variance and the .11 favorable variance (.82 - .11 = .71). So this variance actually helped you.

If your employer looks only at Paid MH/Stat, then being under budget on non-prod hours can sometimes mask overages of worked MH/Stat. If non-prod hours are over budget, then refer to the discussion of *Possibility #4* above for help in addressing and understanding it. You may need to get a detail of the non-prod hours in this situation so you can explain them. If you had several employees attending education classes for a new software install, for example, that kind of incident could explain your variance.

There's more. Line 13 shows that the *Average Hourly Rate* (AHR) was over budget. The AHR is simply the overall average rate paid for the period. It is computed by dividing the gross salary cost by the total hours paid in the period. If there are more than a few people in the department that have differing pay rates, this number will likely be slightly different each pay period. Here are two of the most common reasons why:

1. A shift in skill mix. If person A is paid $10/hr and works 20 hours, and person B is paid $20/hr and works 20 hours, then the AHR will be [($10 x 20) + ($20 x 20)] / 40 hours = $15. But if there is even the slightest shift, the average will change. If Person A works 25 hours, and person B works 15 hours, then the average paid for the same 40 hours is $13.75. How might this apply to your department? If you have support staff paid at lower hourly rates than your more highly trained staff, then your AHR each period will be affected by what percentage of hours are paid to the higher paid staff compared to the lower paid staff.

2. Premium pay. Even if everyone in the department had the same pay rate, and that pay rate exactly matches the budgeted AHR, you may be affected by premium pay. Remember that premium pay refers to any pay that has a premium associated with it. Overtime and use of contract or registry labor are the two most common reasons for premium pay, but there are others. Shift differential, call or callback pay are three others. Many hospitals have complex "add-ons" to base pay for various reasons. Any time your use of premium pay is different than the budget, your AHR will also vary from budget. Look at line 24 and 26. They show that 367 hours of overtime were worked. 367 hours are 3.5% of the total hours worked. The budget did not allow for any overtime. Line 27 shows

what the AHR would have been without any OT. You can see here that your AHR variance was caused by the OT: the AHR excluding OT is $31.00, against a budget of $31.01. See that? So if you had not incurred any overtime, your AHR would not have been over budget. But instead, the AHR was $31.50. The $.50 difference is the impact of OT on the AHR *(see line 28)*. How much did $.50/hr cost you in terms of salaries? See line 22. It cost you $5,555 for the month. That may not seem like much, but a person making $60,000 a year makes $5,000 per month. So actually, this money could have "bought" you an extra FTE. Maybe you didn't need an extra person in your department, but maybe some other department in the hospital could have. Or maybe another department could have used 2 people who each made $30,000 per year, or 3 people making $20,000 each per year. It adds up pretty quickly, doesn't it? Another way to look at it is that the $.50 per hour was an added 1.6% on the $31.00 per hour you spent without the OT. That money could have paid for over half—yes, half, of a 3% merit raise. Wow! So now when you hear management talking about not having the money available to give merit raises, you can see how you could help your staff and coworkers generate the money to make that possible!

Lines 14, 15, and 16 are input items showing the salary costs of the hours worked. As you can see, you are under budget by $7,177. But look down at rows 20 through 23. Line 23 shows the $7,177 again, but lines 20,21, and 22 show you the break down of it. Line 20 "$$$ Impact of Volume Variance," shows you that because volume was less than budget, if you had been able to adjust staffing and achieve the 9.79 budgeted MH/Stat *(shown in the budget column of line 12)*, you would have saved $36,431. Line 21 shows that the "extra" MH/Stat applied to the volume that you did have, cost an extra $23,698. Does that make sense to you? Line 20 is the savings you should have achieved by having 120 fewer patient days than budget. Line 21 is the extra money you spent by having the extra .71 MH/Stat for each of the 1,080 patient days you did have. And as we already discussed, line 22 shows the extra $5,555 you spent by using overtime.

Lines 17, 18, and 19 show the Cost per UOS. You can see on line 19 that the total cost per UOS is $330.67; $27.09 over budget. The good news is that it could have been worse: the Worked $$ per UOS was $30.19 over, but the Non-Prod cost was under by $3.13, giving the net of $27.09.

Why does the Cost per Unit of Service matter? Hopefully, you know the answer to this question by now. We've discussed it. It is because revenue is tied to volume, so expenses need to be too. We need to manage costs relative to the revenue we earn. When the budget was prepared, a cost of $303.59 (line 19) was set as the target amount we could spend compared to the revenue we would earn. Actually, cost per UOS is the most important statistic to manage. It is more important than MH/stat. As a CFO, I am not concerned if you spent more time getting the tasks done in your department as long as you still got it done within the amount of money budgeted per task (department statistic).

So now maybe you are feeling like you did blow it? Even though your hours and dollars are less than budget, neither is under budget as much as volume was *under* budget.

Did you blow it? Maybe. But it's not time to throw in the towel yet. Remember our discussion about labor never being completely variable? I deliberately picked a Nursing unit for this example because we spent so much time building the nursing budget and showing how changes in volumes can dramatically impact productivity. Remember this discussion? I'll assume you do (or if you didn't, you've already refreshed your memory by re-visiting the chapter, and you're now back with me!). It actually applies to any department that is budgeted as either variable or partially variable. Here we will apply it to nursing because we have data on nursing elsewhere that we can refer to. But even if you are not a nursing manager, this discussion can still be applied to your department.

Look at **Exhibit 21** *(page 142)* again. Look at line 10 again: Worked MH/Stat is over budget (9.72 actual on a budget of 8.90) by .82. But, look, too, at the budgeted ADC, and the Actual ADC for the month of April. The budgeted ADC was 40, and the actual was 36. Now, go back to **Exhibit 10** *(page 77)*. Remember, this is where the staffing matrix is translated into a worked MH/Stat Productivity number. The column on the far left is the census, and the column on the far right is the worked MH/Stat. Find the budgeted census of 40 on the left, and follow across with your finger to the far right, and you will see the worked MH/Stat of 8.90, which is the budgeted stat in **Exhibit 21**. But you did not have an ADC of 40. You had an ADC of 36. Repeat the exercise of looking at **Exhibit 10**, except this time find the row for a census of 36, and follow THAT line across. You will see that the staffing matrix provides for worked MH/Stat of 9.89 when census is only 36. Aha! Your worked MH/Stat was only 9.72 (as shown on **Exhibit 21** on row 10 in the "Actual" column) on a census of 36, when the staffing matrix called for a worked MH/Stat of 9.89 on a census of 36. So you actually BEAT the productivity budget, when it is adjusted for volume (remember, with productivity—less is better).

So you have the answer to the question of why you were over budget:

a. Census was lower than budget, causing inefficiencies. Your worked MH/Stat was actually lower than the care matrix shows for what the actual census was.

b. Non-Prod time was actually under budget.

c. The cost per UOS was over budget because of a) the lower census inefficiencies, and b) the increase in the AHR caused by the unbudgeted use of OT. (you need to be able to explain why OT was necessary).

Let's look briefly at another example. Similar scenario, but different issues.

Look at **Exhibit 22** *(page 148)*. This exhibit is identical to **Exhibit 21**, except the month is now May (with 31 days), and volume exceeded budget. Labor costs, MH/Stat, Cost per UOS are all over budget. The only good news we see is that there was no OT, and AHR is right on budget. So let's look at the other issues together, and break them down.

First, look at non-prod time and the associated data: 432 hours over budget *(line 4)*, 2.45 FTEs over budget (line 8), .18 MH/Stat over budget *(line 11)*, $13,381 over budget *(line 15)*, $5.62 per UOS over budget *(line 18)*.

Ouch! 432 hours over budget on a budget of 1,068. That is a 40% variance! I would assume that with that level of overages, you would know why. If your hospital considers orientation time non-prod, then maybe you have new staff on orientation. Maybe it is summer and folks went on vacation (maybe the budget "forgot" to adjust for high vacation seasons such as Memorial Day). Maybe someone went out unexpectedly on FMLA. All of these are things that you would know because you deal with the issues every day. Remember— finance-ese simply tells the story of what happened. *Your* story.

Now look at productive time and associated data. Worked hours and FTEs are over budget. But remember volume was over budget, too. Is *that* why labor is over budget? What can you look at to answer that question? Why, productivity of course!

How does the worked MH/Stat look compared to budget? Oh dear! It's over budget too. Remember that earlier we discussed productivity being over budget because the *volume* variance was less than the hours variance? At that time, we were looking at a department with census less than budget, and we were talking about sometimes not being able to flex staffing 100% with volume, so when volume drops you cannot reduce staffing by the same amount. Remember that discussion? Here, the exact same principal applies, except in reverse. In this situation, the volume was *up* compared to budget, but the hours were up *more*. This results then, in the worked MH/Stat being over budget.

We are using a Nursing unit for this discussion, but remember, it can apply to *any* department. As we discussed earlier, if your department is semi-variable, or has fluctuating volumes and fixed staff—normally volume being up will *improve* productivity. You have staff working inefficiently because you have excess capacity. So when volume increases, staffing levels don't need to, and productivity improves: staff become more efficient.

So what happened? "Aha," you say. Let's go look at the staffing matrix. Let's see how the worked MH/Stat compares to the staffing matrix when ADC is 45. Maybe that will explain it?

Go back once more to **Exhibit 10** *(page 77)*, and look once more across the row where census is 45. What is the MH/Stat supposed to be? It is 8.98. See that on the far right? So last month at a census of 45, you should have run a

	EXHIBIT 22				
	Nursing Unit A				
	Productivity Report				
	Department Stat		Patient Days + Equivalent Observation Days		
				May 2010	
Line	Description	Formula	Actual	Budget	More/(Less)
1	Total UOS	Input	1,400	1,200	200
2	ADC	line 1 / days in month	45	40	5
3	Total Worked Hours	Input	13,020	10,680	2,340
4	Total non-Prod Hours	Input	1,500	1,068	432
5	Total Paid Hours	line 3 + line 4	14,521	11,748	2,772
6	Hours per FTE	2,080/365 x # days in month	176.66	176.66	-
7	Worked FTEs	line 3 / line 6	73.70	60.46	13.25
8	Non-Prod FTEs	line 4 / line 6	8.49	6.05	2.45
9	Total Paid FTEs	line 5 / line 6	82.19	66.50	15.69
10	Worked MH/Stat	line 3 / line 1	9.30	8.90	0.40
11	Non-Prod MH/Stat	line 4 / line 1	1.07	0.89	0.18
12	Total Paid MH/Stat	line 5 / line 1	10.37	9.79	0.58
13	Average Hourly Rate	line 16 / line 5	$31.00	$31.01	$(0.01)
14	Cost of Worked FTEs	Input	$403,620	$331,187	$72,433
15	Cost of Non-Prod FTEs	Input	$46,500	$33,119	$13,381
16	Total Cost of FTEs	Input	$450,151	$364,305	$85,846
17	Worked Cost per UOS	line 14 / line 1	$288.30	$275.99	$12.31
18	Non-Prod Cost per UOS	line 15 / line 1	$33.21	$27.60	$5.62
19	Total Cost per UOS	line 16 / line 1	$321.54	$303.59	$17.95
20	$$ Impact of Volume Variance	line 1 more/(less) column x line 19 budget column			$60,718
21	$$ Impact of MH/Stat Variance	line 12 more/(less) column x line 1 actual x line 13 budget			$25,273
22	$$ Impact of AHR Variance	line 13 more/(less) column x line 5 actual column			$(145)
23	Total Variance				$85,846
24	Overtime Hours	Input	-	-	-
25	Total Worked Hours	From line 3 above	13,020	10,680	2,340
26	Overtime %	line 24 / line 25	0.0%	0.0%	0.0%
27	AHR excluding OT	line 16 / [(line 5 - line 24) + (1.5 x line 24)]	31.00	31.01	(0.01)
28	Impact of OT on AHR	line 13 - line 27	-	-	-

worked MH/Stat of 8.98, and you ran 9.30. The budget at a budgeted census of 40 was 8.90 worked MH/Stat. Lots of numbers. Confused? Ok. Let's go over it again.

a. At a budgeted census of 40, the worked MH/Stat was budgeted to be 8.90

b. At a census of 45, the worked MH/Stat (per the staffing matrix) should be 8.98

c. At a census of 45, your worked MH/Stat came in at 9.30.

So although your TOTAL variance is the difference between 9.30 actual and 8.90 budget (c-a), the difference between 8.90 and 8.98(b-a) is explained by the staffing matrix. So your *unexplained* variance is only the difference between the staffing matrix at a census of 45 (8.98), and your *Actual* MH/Stat at a census of 45, which was 9.30 (c-b). I know that may seem like a very long and confusing paragraph with a lot of numbers. Re-read it slowly as many times as you need to in order to understand. This is a very key concept to understand. Move on whenever you are ready.

So how big of a variance is the difference between the 8.98 and the 9.30? Again, whether or not your hospital will consider this "material" (a big enough variance that you are expected to explain it) is up to them. My rule is 5%. Is 9.30 more than 5% greater than 8.98? 9.30 / 8.98 is 1.035. That means 9.30 is only 3.5% greater than 8.98, so the answer is no. But if it was, how would you go about looking at this?

First, how many hours or FTEs make up the difference between 9.30 and 8.98? The formula to figure that out is:

MH/Stat difference x UOS = Excess hours
Excess hours / # hours per FTE = Excess FTEs

So let's apply that:

(9.30—8.98) x 1400 = 448 excess hours
448 excess hours / 176.66 hr per FTE
= 2.54 FTEs

Now the question to answer is *why did you have 448 excess hours, or 2.54 extra FTEs?* Think back over the month. You probably know the answer. Remember—this is *worked* hours only. So folks being out for vacation, etc. does not apply. Here are some possibilities to think about:

a. **Sitters:** If this is a Nursing unit—what about sitters? Notice there are none budgeted in the staffing matrix used in this book. Look at your own budget matrix to see if it provides for any. If not, do you keep a log of sitter hours? Did you have 448 hours? Maybe you had 200 hours. Which means you only have 248 more hours you need to explain.

b. **Orientation:** If your hospital records orientation hours as worked hours, how many hours of orientation did you have?

c. **Discharge Timing (get them out early!):** Another possibility for a Nursing unit is discharge timing. The productivity stat is probably based on UOS taken from the midnight census. If your census is higher in the middle of the day because new patients have been admitted, but the discharges for the day are not gone yet, then you need extra staff in the middle of the day. If your RN ratio if 5:1, then for each ten extra patients you have in the middle of the day compared to the midnight census, you would need two RNs, and probably another PCA. Think about that for a minute. I've just told you how you may be able to explain your variance, but I will also warn you that if that is happening on your unit, it is an issue you need to address. It's probably an issue that will require many people to help address (physicians, case management, etc), but it needs to be addressed. If this is the reason for your 448 excess hours, then this problem cost you 448 hours x $31.00/hr = $13,888 just in this month alone! Do you remember why this would be important? Remember that payments (revenue) are based on the midnight census. So if you have a patient that is inhouse and cared for all day, but then leaves at, say, 6 p.m., then you have incurred all the costs associated with a day of care, and there will be no revenue to cover it. That is why hospitals push for discharges before noon.

d. **Daily Volume Swings:** Even if you aren't a Nursing unit, you may also have an issue of the timing of your volume skewing productivity—in a different way. Remember that when volume exceeds budget, you usually have the ability to be more productive, but if volume is less than budget, you may become less efficient because you have core staff? What if volume swings wildly in your department? Look at **Exhibit 23** *(next page)*. Start by looking at the "Total" columns on the right. This example shows two days of productivity. Over the two-day period, volume in total was exactly equal to budget. But you were over budget in your man hours, causing an unfavorable productivity variance. You have been asked to explain it. So now let's look at the individual days. On day 1, your volume was very high—150 units of service on a budget of 100. you were able to beat the budgeted productivity because you only needed to add 25 more worked hours to provide the added 50 units of service. But on day 2, the reverse happened. Volume was only 50 units of service. Because you have core staffing requirements, you did not have the ability to flex staffing down, so that productivity for the day was 2.0 on a budget of 1.0. The result over the 2 days is that the sum of the 2 days volume is exactly equal to budget, but productivity is over budget. So what could you do to address this issue? The answer depends on your department and situation. OB units frequently have this issue. Volume is very unpredictable, but regulatory requirements mandate minimum staffing levels at all times. In this situation, there is probably not much that can be done. But what if you run an imaging department with lower

EXHIBIT 23									
	Day 1			Day 2			Total		
	Actual	Budget	Variance	Actual	Budget	Variance	Actual	Budget	Variance
Units of Service	150	100	50	50	100	(50)	200	200	-
Worked Man Hours	125	100	25	100	100	-	225	200	25
Worked MH/Stat	0.83	1.00	(0.17)	2.00	1.00	1.00	1.13	1.00	0.13

volumes than the example and day one was Friday, and day two was Saturday? You may be able to look at historical volumes on weekends, and see that volume is always very low. In that case, you may be able to consider either reducing staff on weekends, or change staffing to have people on call instead of staffed to work. A very simple model you may be able to use to estimate the financial impact of that decision is shown in **Exhibit 24**.

WORK OR CALL?

Exhibit 24 shows a simple model you may be able to use to help you decide whether you should schedule staff to work, or use call to provide coverage. For some departments and situations, call is not an option. But when it is, this model will at least show you the financial ramifications of your choices.

The example shown in **Exhibit 24** is a very simple example of a very small department with extremely low volume—similar to what might happen on a weekend. The information you need to prepare the analysis is shown on the left. The two numerical columns illustrate how to make the determination.

EXHIBIT 24		
	Scheduled To Work	Scheduled For Call
Units of Service	3	3
Worked Man Hours	8	3
On Call hours	-	5
Total covered hours	8	8
Rate per worked hour	$20.00	$20.00
Callback premium per hour	N/A	$10.00
Callpay per hour	N/A	$3.00
Worked hours pay	$160.00	$60.00
Premium Pay for callback	$-	$30.00
Call Pay	$-	$15.00
Total Cost	$160.00	$105.00

In this example, only three units of service are needed on this weekend day. You may either pay someone to work eight hours, or put someone on call. The person on call will be paid $3 per hour for each hour that he/she is NOT called. In our example, the staff is called and must come in three times, for a total of three hours. The scenario where the staff *works* costs $160 (8 hours at $20). Under the *on-call* scenario, the person is paid $20 for the three hours that he had to work, plus an extra $10 call premium for the same three hours, plus he is paid $3 per hour for the remaining five hours that he was on call, but not called in. Therefore, his total pay is

$105—which is less than the $160 paid to have someone work—a $55 and 35% savings! Call is always a financial gamble, and it has drawbacks because the person is not instantly available. But if you can imagine the 35% savings applied to a larger scale, over 104 weekend days, and 365 nights, you can see why it may be worth looking into!

CONTROLLABLE VS NON-CONTROLLABLE VARIANCES

Let's go back and look at **Exhibit 22** *(page 148)* again for a moment. Look at *Lines 20 through 23*. You see that in total, salaries are $85,846 over budget. But volumes were over budget, you say! Yes, they were. But is that the only driver of the excess salary expenses? Will the excess salaries be covered by the excess revenues that should be generated by the extra volume? Let's take a look. The reason I put this breakdown in the book is to demonstrate to you controllable vs non-controllable variances. Why does this matter? As a CFO, I would only expect to hold you accountable for Controllable variances.

Non-Controllable variances are those caused by volumes being different than budget. Generally speaking, if you are a good nursing manager, you don't control the census in your department: you have no control over what comes in, and you manage the patients that do come in as efficiently as possible, and discharge them when they are ready to leave. So if your volume is either greater or less than budget, you do not control that, and nor do you control the resulting increase or decrease in staffing that (in a perfect world) goes with those fluctuations. Let me give you three very simple examples to demonstrate:

a. If you were budgeted to care for two patients one day, and each patient was to receive ten hours of care, at $30/hr, then your budget would be 2 x 10 x $30 = $600. If three patients actually came in, and you gave each patient ten hours of care at $30/hour, then your actual expense would be 3 x 10 x $30 = $900. the difference between the $600 budget, and the $900 expense is a *Non-Controllable* variance. You did everything you were supposed to do. The variance is caused by something that you do not control—volume. Applying this principal to **Exhibit 22**, look at *line 20*—it shows that salaries were over budget by $60,718. This is the amount of extra money that needed to be spent because there were more patient days than budgeted.

b. If you were budgeted to care for two patients one day, and each patient was to receive ten hours of care at $30/hr, again, your budget would be $600. But let's say only one patient came in, and you did not adjust staffing, and still spent $600. In a perfect world, if you only care for one patient, then you should have reduced staffing and only spent 10 hours x 1 patient x $30/hr = $300. The difference between what you spent and what you should have spent is a *controllable* variance—one you are responsible to manage or explain. In this case, this was a *productivity* variance. It was not caused by the AHR being higher than budget. In both cases the AHR was $30. The variance is caused by too many hours per patient day being worked. Productivity variances may be partially or wholly caused by staffing matrix differences (as we demonstrated on **Exhibit 21** (*page 141*), but they are considered to be *controllable* because you control productivity. Applying this principal to **Exhibit 22** (*page 148*), look at line 21—it shows that salaries were over by $25,273. this is the amount of extra money spent because extra hours per patient day were spent caring for the patients. As we already discussed, some of these extra hours are the result of staffing matrix differences, but there were 448 "unexplained" hours in the department that you would need to explain. These dollars reflect those excess hours.

c. If you were budgeted to care for two patients one day, and each patient was to receive ten hours of care at $30/hr, again, your budget would be $600. Let's say you did take care of two patients at ten hours of care per patient. But you used contract labor or overtime instead, so the cost was $45/hr. This means you spent 2 x 10 x $45 = $900 instead of the budgeted $600. This too is a *controllable* variance,one that you are responsible to manage or explain. In this case, this was a rate variance. It was not caused by too many hours being worked per patient day—it was simply caused by the higher rate of pay. Rate variances can be caused by differences in skill mixes (more higher paid nurses and fewer lower paid support staff than budgeted), or use of unbudgeted premium labor (overtime, callback or contract labor). To demonstrate this principal, look back at **Exhibit 21** (*page 141*) instead of **Exhibit 22** (*page 148*). Look at *line 22*—it shows salaries were over budget by $5,555 due to a rate variance. You remember that in this example (*see line 24*) 367 hours of OT were worked on a budget of zero. If this had not happened, salaries would have been $5,555 less than they were.

PRODUCTIVITY ACCURACY AND MONTH-END PAYROLL ACCRUALS

More and more hospitals now report productivity every day. If your hospital reports every day, then it most likely pulls the data from your payroll system. I'm sure you've heard the expression "garbage in, garbage out." We've talked about the importance of capturing all the charges and all of the hours for your department each day (or however often productivity is reported). If time is missing from the payroll system, then your productivity report will be inaccurate. It will also be inaccurate if department statistics are inaccurate. If your hospital feels productivity is important enough to report it daily, they probably have policies and procedures for reporting it. And as I've said before, the information may be being used for things you do not even know about.

Even if your productivity is not hitting budgeted targets, it is much better to be honest than to have a surprise at the end of the pay period when you must true it up!

There is one twist in productivity reporting I feel I need to warn you about. It's the month end accrual. I apologize, but we need to have a brief accounting lesson before we can discuss it.

At the end of each month, as part of the closing process, the folks in finance must record an expense for employee payroll. For pay periods that ended during the month, it is easy. After all, accounting processed those paychecks, so they know exactly how much they spent. But most months, the pay period does not end on the last day of the month. So accounting is left to make an estimate as to what expense was incurred between the last day of the most recent pay period, and the last day of the month. Let's say the most recent 14-day pay period ended of the 26th of April (a 30-day month). The next pay period will end of the 10th of the next month.

But accounting cannot wait until then to close the books for the month. So they must estimate what payroll expense was for the four days April 27, 28, 29, and 30th. Unfortunately, most accounting systems have a very unsophisticated way of doing this. The accounting system usually takes the hours and dollars from the most recent pay period and divides it by the number of days the pay period covered (in our example, it is 14 days). This calculation gives a "daily rate." The daily rate is then multiplied by the number of days that need to be accrued (in our example, four days). That amount becomes the accrual. So the accounting system assumes that the productivity of the last four days of the pay period equals the *daily* average of the previous pay period. Although from an overall hospital perspective, this calculation generally results in an accrual that is materially correct, there are many times when that assumption could be significantly wrong for an individual department. What if your department is closed on the weekends, and two of those four days at the end of the month were a weekend? Or what if those last four days included a holiday when you would have had many people out? Or if the previous pay period included a holiday so it over stated the hours for the last 4 days?

The point of all of this is to alert you. If you review productivity daily, there is a good chance that the productivity statistics you see on your month-end reports will be different. One month they may be too high, followed by a month when they are too low (the amount that the accrual was off in one month always self-corrects the next month). If you see a significant difference, you may want to ask accounting how many days were included in the accrual at month-end this month and compare the accrued amount to the actual productivity. Because each month also includes a true-up from the previous month, this reconciliation can get a bit messy.

Chapter 13 Self Review Questions

1. If you are a department managed as a "Fixed" department, what does that mean for labor management purposes?

2. What are the numerator and denominator used for labor productivity?

3. Name the six possible reasons a fixed department's productivity may be off from budget.

4. If volume is higher than budget in a department with fixed staffing, will productivity be over or under budget?

5. If your labor management report shows that your MH/stat is over budget, while your cost per UOS is under budget, will your CFO be upset?

Monitoring Other Expenses

Up to this point, we've talked about monitoring volumes and labor. That means that for the purposes of this chapter, everything else falls into "Other Expenses." Supplies. Maintenance and Repairs, Outside Services. Rentals. There is no easy, systematic way to monitor these expenses.

Expenditures are rolling through the department, probably every day. Depending on your hospital's approval processes, you may or may not see them or approve them in advance unless they cost more than $XXX. If you can imagine keeping a log of every expense, that is really the only thing you can do. Unless you are a small department, that is probably not even feasible. But you do want to do *something*. Why? Because if you don't monitor during the month, how will you know at the end of the month if your financial statements are correct? So what can you do?

For supply expenses, your materials folks may be able to get you reports showing everything that has been issued to you. Or the Purchasing folks may be able to get you reports of what you have ordered. The only thing you can do is to review (peruse) them for anything that looks wrong or inappropriate. For example, the admitting department would not expect to see a supply expense for surgical draping. If you feel like your expenses are incorrect month after month, then by all means you should talk to materials about the processes to make sure that they have controls in place to ensure you are charged for all, but only, what you order.

For pretty much everything else, all you can really do is monitor and track large, unusual items so that at the end of the month you can look to see if those expenses are accurately reflected. For example, if you work in Dietary, and your grill goes out and needs a very expensive repair, you will want to make note of it somewhere. However is easiest for you. You may make a log that you record these types of things in, or maybe you keep a folder and make copies of the invoices when they come in. But then you must keep up to make sure you do get invoiced timely. Otherwise, you may get a "surprise" expense a few months down the road when the invoice that got lost suddenly shows up. Believe me— finance will be even more unhappy than you!

Depending on your hospital's approval process, your CFO may or may not be required to approve these types of large items. Just to be safe, you will likely want to inform him. At the very least, ask him at what level he wants you to inform him. If your hospital does mid-month projections, he will need to know these types of things.

Chapter 14 Self Review Questions

1. Why should you monitor expenses other than labor during the month?

2. Name one way to keep track of other expenses.

3. Why is it important to keep the CFO informed of large or unusual expenses that are being incurred?.

Section IV
Month End Review

Overview

Are you held accountable for the financial performance of your department(s)? I'm assuming you are. If you are, then month-end is when it all comes together. Back in **Chapter** 4 we talked about the purpose of a budget. That a budget was a one-year slice of the strategic plan, sliced into 12 monthly budgets, and the purpose was to allow you to monitor how you were doing against that plan? That makes it important to check each month and see how it's going.

Remember our example of you opening a coffee shop? You had a plan for which month you would open, how much coffee you would sell, how many employees you would have. Month end is a time to stop, step back and see how you are doing against that plan. Maybe unforeseen obstacles have arisen and you are behind. Or maybe you are right on track, or even beating the plan. If you own a small business, you may know the answers to these questions everyday. If you own or manage a large organization (or department), probably not. Whether you intuitively know how you're doing or not, the month end close process "documents" what happened. Puts your story on paper for the month. When you put each month together over the course of the year, you have a diary of how you got from where you started at the beginning of the year to where you are at the end.

The purpose of this section is to help you understand the process that takes place behind the scenes, and then help you understand how to "read" your story as you review your financials. I promise to keep the accounting lessons to the absolute minimum required!

Understanding Accruals

I know. I know. I promised that this would not be a book about accounting. I've tried to keep the accounting lessons to a minimum. But there is one more lesson we need to go over. It's the last one, and perhaps the most relevant to you. If you do review your department financial statements every month, it will certainly be the one piece of accounting knowledge that you will use over and over again. So I apologize that it will probably be very boring to most of you. And it is very dry. Please bear with me. I'll try to get through it as quickly as I can. And we need to do it before we can talk about reviewing your monthly financial statements. So let's get it out of the way.

There are two ways to keep the accounting books: Cash basis or Accrual basis.

Cash basis accounting is very straightforward. Financial statements are presented based simply on cash transactions. Revenue is recognized when the money is collected—regardless of when the goods or services were provided. Expenses are recognized when the bills are paid, regardless of when the goods or services were received.

Accrual accounting, on the other hand, requires recognition of revenue and expenses when the goods or services are provided or received; both are regardless of when the cash was received or paid.

To understand the difference between the two accounting approaches, perhaps it would help to explain that all accounting systems are basically set up to function on a cash basis; that is, without intervention, accounting principles will capture every event on a cash basis. Similar to your own personal finances, you probably do not write a journal entry to capture using electricity (that would be accrual basis accounting), but you do capture paying the bill when you write the check (that would be cash basis accounting), since even if you do not "keep your own books," the bank keeps cash basis accounting books for you: It's called your bank statement. Applying accrual basis accounting, therefore, requires *extra* intervention.

Let's look at a very simple illustration to show what added work is required to capture accrual basis accounting.

See **Exhibit 25**. Here, services are provided to a patient by employees on 4/10/2010. And electricity is used to provide the services. The employees are paid on 4/21/2010. The electric bill is received in May, 2010, but isn't paid until 6/15/2010, and the money (revenue) from the patient's insurance company does not arrive until 5/29/2010.

If accrual basis accounting is used, all three activities are reflected on the April financial statements. If cash basis accounting is used, then the only activity reflected in April is the payments to the employees. The revenue for services to the patient is reflected when it is collected in May, and the expense of the electric bill is not reflected until the June financial statements when it is paid.

The root of accrual accounting is the concept of *matching* the revenue earned with the expenses or resources utilized to earn it. Going back to your coffee shop example in **Chapter 4**, you can see that an investor would be quite confused if he was trying to determine how operations were going if he only saw a cash basis financial statement. That is not to say that cash flow isn't just as important, which is why organizations that use accrual basis accounting also have a second financial statement: a cash flow statement.

So why do you need to know this? In **Chapter 3**, we described Generally Accepted Accounting Principles ("GAAP"), that "rule book" that accountants live by. Well, most companies are required to follow GAAP rules for *accrual basis* accounting. But when you review your month-end financial statements

EXHIBIT 25							
				Accrual Basis			
Activity	Date of Activity	Date Cash Received/ Paid		April	May	June	Total
Services Provided	4/10/2010	5/29/2010		$1,000	$-	$-	$1,000
Employees work	4/10/2010	4/21/2010		$(500)	$-	$-	$(500)
Electricity used	4/10/2010	6/15/2010		$(100)	$-	$-	$(100)
		Profit/(Loss)		$400	$-	$-	$400
				Cash Basis			
Activity	Date of Activity	Date Cash Received/ Paid		April	May	June	Total
Services Provided	4/10/2010	5/29/2010		$-	$1,000	$-	$1,000
Employees work	4/10/2010	4/21/2010		$(500)	$-	$-	$(500)
Electricity used	4/10/2010	6/15/2010		$-	$-	$(100)	$(100)
		Profit/(Loss)		$(500)	$1,000	$(100)	$400

and are trying to sort through what events were (or were not) charged to you this month, it can get confusing, depending on what reports you use to perform your review.

We've discussed how the cash basis vs accrual basis financial statements *look* different, but I think it will be much more helpful for you to understand how the finance folks make that happen behind the scenes. What are those "extra" steps that must be taken to capture accrual basis accounting? This will be important if you actually drill into your financial results and need to understand what you are looking at. If this doesn't make much sense yet, don't worry. It may be that you won't understand this section now, but will understand it better when you come back to it later.

Accrual accounting management on the revenue side is different than how you manage the expense side. We'll assume that you probably are not too concerned with the revenue side. As long as the revenues show up each day, you're happy. So let's focus on the expense side.

OK, let's get started. If you look again at **Exhibit 25**, you will recall that there were two expenses. The first was the employee labor. Because the expense was incurred and paid in the same month, nothing special needs to be done (the cash basis accounting and the accrual basis accounting are the same). But with the electric bill, you used the $100 of electricity in April. The bill arrived and was keyed into Accounts Payable in May, and then was paid in June. Using **Exhibit 26**, we'll look at each month.

Row	Name	Description	Who?	April	May	June	Total
	EXHIBIT 26						
	Electricity Used:						
1	Accrual	Month end Close	Accounting	$100	$-	$-	$100
2	Accrual Reversal	Day 1 Entry	Automatic	$-	$(100)	$-	$(100)
3	A/P Posting	During the month	Accounts Payable	$-	$100	$(100)	$-
4	Bill paid	During the month	Accounts Payable	$-	$-	$100	$100
5	Total			$100	$-	$-	$100

April: Remember that when you write the check to pay the electric bill, the expense will automatically be captured. But in our example, since the time between when you use the electricity and the time you pay for it spans three months, special intervention is required to capture it in accrual basis accounting. In April, you used the electricity, but since you didn't pay for it, nothing was recorded. In order to capture the expenses, an *accrual* is recorded *(see row 1 on Exhibit 26)*. This accrual is a manual transaction, keyed into the General Ledger (see **Chapter 3**), by the folks in finance as part of the month-end close process. The effect of recording the accrual is that the $100 expense is captured on the April financial statements.

May: In May, in our story, the electric bill for the month of April arrived, and was keyed into the accounts payable system but was not paid. So what does that mean to our lesson? The first lesson for May is the reversal of the accrual. In April, when finance recorded the accrual, they "told" the accounting software that they wanted this entry to be recorded as an accrual. When you "tell" the accounting software that you are entering an entry that you want to be an accrual, you are telling the software that you want the entry you are making to be automatically reversed on the first day of the next month. If you look at the *May* column of **Exhibit 26** *(page 167)*, you see this event happening on row 2. The important thing for you to learn is that, by *the very definition of accrual, every entry recorded as an accrual is automatically reversed by the system on the first day of the following month.* The second lesson for May is that when the bill arrived and was keyed into the Accounts Payable system, an expense was recorded *(see row 3 on* **Exhibit 26**). Oh dear! But we do not want or need an expense recorded. We already accrued for the expense last month. If we let this expense stay recorded, we will have recorded an expense with our accrual in April, and again using the Accounts Payable system in May. Oh—but wait! Remember, our accrual reversed! So there is a "negative" expense from the accrual reversing, plus a "positive" expense from the Accounts Payable system: the two entries net to zero. As a result, when you look at your financial statements, you see zero. Little did you know that the zero you see is actually two entries, huh? And zero is exactly what we want, right? Right.

June: Finally, we are going to pay the electric bill from April in June. When this happens, we take the liability off the accounts payable ledger simultaneous with writing the check. Both of those events are shown on *rows 3 and 4* in the June column of **Exhibit 26**. As you can see, removing the liability from accounts payable and writing the check cancel each other out, so that again, no expense is charged to the month. And again, even though your financial statements show zero (as they should), it isn't because there was no activity, it is because zero is the net amount of all of the transactions. That may be important for you to remember. When you look at your financial statements, whether you are seeing a zero or a number, what you are seeing may be the net effect of several entries.

So as you look across *row 5* of **Exhibit 26**, you can see that in April you used electricity and you recognized the expense. In the other two months, although several activities occurred, none of them "showed up" on your financial statements. That is the way accrual basis accounting should work.

I know, you are really bored, and think you do not need to know all of this. So to help you understand why you *do* need to know all this, I want to walk you through an example where the accounting entries are not made correctly. Then you can see what happens. Remember, the finance folks *do* make mistakes every now and then. So it is important for you to understand what *could* go wrong. That way, if your financial statements appear to contain a mistake, you will have some idea of what it might be and why it might have occurred.

		EXHIBIT 27						
					The Wrong Way			
Row	Name	Description	Who?	April	May	June	Total
	Electricity Used:						
1	Accrual	Month end Close	Accounting	$100	$-	$-	$100
2	Accrual Reversal	Day 1 Entry	Automatic	$-	$(100)	$-	$(100)
3	A/P Posting	During the month	Accounts Payable	$-	$-	$100	$100
4	A/P Posting	During the month	Accounts Payable			$(100)	$(100)
5	Bill paid	During the month	Accounts Payable	$-	$-	$100	$100
6	**Total**			$100	$(100)	$100	$100

					The Right Way			
Row	Name	Description	Who?	April	May	June	Total
	Electricity Used:						
7	Accrual	Month end Close	Accounting	$100	$100	$-	$200
8	Accrual Reversal	Day 1 Entry	Automatic	$-	$(100)	$(100)	$(200)
9	A/P Posting	During the month	Accounts Payable	$-	$-	$100	$100
10	A/P Posting	During the month	Accounts Payable			$(100)	$(100)
11	Bill paid	During the month	Accounts Payable	$-	$-	$100	$100
12	**Total**			$100	$-	$-	$100

Look at **Exhibit 27**. At first glance, it looks very similar to **Exhibit 26** *(page 167)*. I thought it might be helpful to use the same example. However, in **Exhibit 27**, you notice there are two presentations: "The Wrong Way," and "The Right Way." In both scenarios, things begin the same as they did before. You utilize electricity in April. Because the bill has not arrived by the end of the month, an accrual is recorded *(see rows 1 and 7)*. However, in this example, let's say that the bill got lost in the mailroom, and does not get delivered to accounting in May at all. Look at "The Wrong Way" presentation. You see on row 2 that the accrual recorded in April reverses, but there is no entry by accounts payable to offset it. So at the end of the month, there is a negative expense. The problem continues in June. Only routine entries are made to record the invoice in accounts payable, then reverse it and pay the bill, and the net of all those entries is another $100 of expense. When you look across all three months, the total expense is correct at $100, but two of the three months are incorrect.

Now compare "The Wrong Way" with "The Right Way." What should have happened? As silly as it sounds, one simple entry was missed. If someone had reviewed the May financials and seen the error, another accrual would have been booked in May *(see the shaded $100 on row 7)*. That entry would have offset the negative expenses, making it zero in May. Then the accrual would have reversed in June, making the June expense zero, as well *(see the shaded* *negative $100 on row 8).* Again, the total over the three months is $100, but this time all three months are correct.

OK, I'm done. Again, don't feel bad if you don't think you grasped this material very well. As simply as I've tried to present it, this is a bit of geeky accounting. But come back and look at it again next time you think your financial statements don't look right. I find that many times, I can't understand something until I need to use the information. It's a bit like someone giving you driving directions. You may not understand them until you are actually behind the wheel and driving.

Chapter 16 Self Review Questions

1. Name the two types of accounting.

2. With no intervention, which type of accounting will your financial statements reflect?

3. If an expense is incurred in April, the invoice is entered into Accounts Payable in May, and paid in June, with no intervention, in what month will the expense show up on the financial statements?

4. If a $100 expense is incurred in April, the invoice is entered into Accounts Payable in June, and paid in July, if the expense is accrued in April, but not re-accrued in May, what will the May expense reflect?

5. Using the example from #4 above, what activity should the General ledger show for the month of June if everything was done correctly?

CHAPTER 17

Financial Reporting

Before we can start discussing the analysis of your financial statements, I want to spend some time going over two reports you will probably use to perform your month-end review: your **Departmental Income Statement and a Monthly Operating Review** (MOR). What do these reports look like, and how do you read them? In this chapter I will not get into actually looking at what the reports are telling us *(what the story is)*, just how they might be laid out and what information they will most likely contain.

Every company has their own reports, so the examples I use will definitely be different than the ones your hospital uses. But in all my years in hospital accounting, the information contained in the reports is almost always the s ame. You will want to take what you learn here and apply it to your own hospital's reports.

DEPARTMENTAL INCOME STATEMENT

Let's start with the Departmental Income Statement. **Exhibit 28** *(next page)* shows a sample Departmental Income Statement. As indicated at the top, it is for the Radiology department for the month of May, 2011. As always, I've numbered the rows and lettered the columns to make it easier for us to talk about things.

The first thing to do is to compare this report to **Exhibit 15** *(pages 98, 99)*, which was the budget for this same department. If you look down the rows on the left of **Exhibit 28**, you will notice that they are identical to **Exhibit 15**. You will also notice if you look down the "May" column of **Exhibit 15**, and compare it to the "Budget" column *(column B)* of **Exhibit 28** that they also match. If you were really bored, and wanted to add up all of the "Budget" columns from October through May on **Exhibit 15**, you would also see that the total of those columns matches the Year to Date Budget column *(column E)* on **Exhibit 28**.

So, hopefully, you now at least have your bearings. As I've said before, this is simply my example. The format and the names of the rows on your hospital's report will be different. It may contain more or less information than shown in my example.

Looking across the columns, you will see there are two sets of numbers. There are three columns for the "Current Month," and then three more columns for the "Year to Date." Each set of three columns is the same: "Actual," "Budget," and "Variance." The "Variance" column is the result of a formula showing the difference between the Actual and the Budgeted activity.

In my examples, I have the formulas set up in such a way that a negative number is always an unfavorable variance. So *if actual revenue is less than budget, the variance column shows brackets* (since that is an undesired variance because it

	EXHIBIT 28					
1	J Lee Community Hospital					
2	Radiology Department					
3	Fiscal year 2011					
4	Month ending May 31, 2011					
5							
6	Column	A	B	C	D	E	F
7		Current Month			Year to Date		
8		Actual	Budget	Variance	Actual	Budget	Variance
9	**Dept Stat - Exams:**						
10	Inpatient Exams	3,348	3,100	248	21,427	24,300	(2,873)
11	Outpatient Exams	3,949	4,030	(81)	37,914	31,590	6,324
12	Total Exams	7,297	7,130	167	59,341	55,890	3,451
13							
14	**Revenues:**						
15	Gross Inpatient revenues	$1,432,944	$1,240,000	$192,944	$8,785,152	$9,720,000	$(934,848)
16	Gross Outpatient revenues	$1,382,290	$1,612,000	$(229,710)	$14,407,411	$12,636,000	$1,771,411
17	Total Gross Revenues	$2,815,234	$2,852,000	$(36,766)	$23,192,563	$22,356,000	$836,563
18							
19	Revenue Deductions	$-	$-	$-	$-	$-	$-
20							
21	Net Revenues	$2,815,234	$2,852,000	$(36,766)	$23,192,563	$22,356,000	$836,563
22							
23	**Expenses:**						
24	Hospital Salaries	$198,433	$205,629	$7,196	$1,739,891	$1,588,104	$(151,787)
25	Contract labor	$15,987	$-	$(15,987)	$72,397	$-	$(72,397)
26	Benefits	$-	$-	$-	$-	$-	$-
27	Supplies	$20,693	$19,821	$(871)	$161,670	$155,374	$(6,296)
28	Maintenance and Repairs	$1,500	$12,000	$10,500	$82,356	$96,000	$13,644
29	Outside Services	$-	$3,200	$3,200	$21,741	$25,600	$3,859
30	Rental Expense	$-	$-	$-	$-	$-	$-
31	Depreciation	$-	$-	$-	$-	$-	$-
32	Interest	$-	$-	$-	$-	$-	$-
33	Property Taxes	$-	$-	$-	$-	$-	$-
34	Insurance	$-	$-	$-	$-	$-	$-
35	Other Expenses	$500	$1,500	$1,000	$11,000	$12,000	$1,000
36	Total Expenses	$237,113	$242,151	$5,038	$2,089,054	$1,877,078	$(124,241)
37							
38	**Net Margin**	$2,578,121	$2,609,849	$(31,728)	$21,103,509	$20,478,922	$624,587

reduces net income), but *if actual expenses are less than budget, then the variance column shows positive numbers* (since that is usually a desired variance because it increases net income).

This approach allows you to quickly scan the report and identify whether variances are favorable or unfavorable. I call it my "Brackets Are Bad" approach. Different hospitals do it differently, though, so you will always need to check.

As I said, we are not going to analyze the numbers here. We'll do that in the next chapter, so I am only going to point out a few things here:

1. The Revenue Deductions row *(row 19)* is blank. You may recall from **Chapter 2** that I said that revenue deductions are not recorded at the department level. That is why you don't see them here. It is *not* because there aren't any. Believe me there are! How large the deductions are varies by hospital, but it's probably safe to say that over 50% of the gross revenues are lost in revenue deductions. We'll talk again in a moment about what that means to you.

2. The Benefit row *(row 26)* is also blank. Benefits include many things. Besides the cost of things like employee medical, dental, vision, and life insurance, benefits also includes things like payroll taxes (such as FICA), and unemployment insurance. Due to the complexities of attempting to calculate the costs specifically associated with individual departments, every hospital but one I have ever worked with records them all together in a separate department. Benefit expense is not an inconsequential cost. Depending on your company's benefit plans and your state requirements for things like unemployment insurance, benefit costs can run anywhere from 15% to 30% of salary costs! In some ways you do not control this expense since you probably are not involved in the decisions about benefit choices, but benefit costs are tied directly to salary costs: when salary costs go up, so do benefit costs. One employee working extra hours does not increase the cost of that one employee's medical insurance, but the extra hours DO increase FICA (payroll tax) costs, and if a new, unbudgeted employee is added, then all benefit costs increase. One hospital I worked with believed that for that reason, department heads should be accountable for at least the cost of FICA, and did charge that to the individual departments.

3. Various other rows are blank. In some cases, it is because there are no costs of that type associated with your department, but in many cases it is because, similar to benefits, the complexities of accurately calculating the costs associated with an individual department are not worth the time. Depreciation, insurance, utilities, and property taxes are examples.

Exhibit 29 and **Exhibit 30** *(pages 176, 177)* present the same information, except **Exhibit 29** is for a Nursing unit and **Exhibit 30** is for an overhead department. As you can see, the format and presentation are the same. The

	EXHIBIT 29					
1	J Lee Community Hospital					
2	Surgical Nursing Unit					
3	Fiscal year 2011					
4	Month ending May 31, 2011					
5							
6	Column	A	B	C	D	E	F
7		Current Month			Year to Date		
8		Actual	Budget	Variance	Actual	Budget	Variance
9	**Dept Stat - Equivalent Patient Days**						
10	Inpatient Days	1,333	1,488	(155)	8,531	9,523	(992)
11	Equivalent Observation Days	155	124	31	1,488	1,190	298
12	Total Equivalent Days	1,488	1,612	(124)	10,019	10,714	(694)
13							
14	**Revenues:**						
15	Gross Inpatient revenues	$1,439,640	$1,636,800	$(197,160)	$9,426,976	$10,475,520	$(1,048,544)
16	Gross Outpatient revenues	$232,500	$186,000	$46,500	$1,636,800	$1,785,600	$(148,800)
17	Total Gross Revenues	$1,672,140	$1,822,800	$(150,660)	$11,063,776	$12,261,120	$(1,197,344)
18							
19	Revenue Deductions	$-	$-	$-	$-	$-	$-
20							
21	Net Revenues	$1,672,140	$1,822,800	$(150,660)	$11,063,776	$12,261,120	$(1,197,344)
22							
23	**Expenses:**						
24	Hospital Salaries	$475,684	$480,360	$4,676	$3,759,605	$4,371,149	$611,544
25	Contract labor	$20,460	$-	$(20,460)	$102,300	$-	$(102,300)
26	Benefits	$-	$-	$-	$-	$-	$-
27	Supplies	$2,277	$2,418	$141	$17,075	$16,070	$(1,004)
28	Maintenance and Repairs	$-	$-	$-	$-	$-	$-
29	Outside Services	$-	$-	$-	$-	$-	$-
30	Rental Expense	$2,350	$3,000	$650	$8,275	$9,550	$1,275
31	Depreciation	$-	$-	$-	$-	$-	$-
32	Interest	$-	$-	$-	$-	$-	$-
33	Property Taxes	$-	$-	$-	$-	$-	$-
34	Insurance	$-	$-	$-	$-	$-	$-
35	Other Expenses	$200	$400	$200	$3,000	$3,200	$200
36	Total Expenses	$500,971	$486,178	$(14,793)	$3,890,254	$4,399,969	$509,715
37							
38	**Net Margin**	$1,171,169	$1,336,622	$(165,453)	$7,173,522	$7,861,151	$(687,629)

	EXHIBIT 30					
1	J Lee Community Hospital					
2	Admitting Department					
3	Fiscal year 2011					
4	Month ending May 31, 2011					
5							
6	Column	A	B	C	D	E	F
7		Current Month			Year to Date		
8		Actual	Budget	Variance	Actual	Budget	Variance
9	**Dept Stat - Registrations**						
10	Registrations	42,466	40,342	2,123	271,781	322,740	(50,959)
11							
12	Total Registrations	42,466	40,342	2,123	271,781	322,740	(50,959)
13							
14	**Revenues:**						
15	Gross Inpatient revenues	$-	$-	$-	$-	$-	$-
16	Gross Outpatient revenues	$-	$-	$-	$-	$-	$-
17	Total Gross Revenues	$-	$-	$-	$-	$-	$-
18							
19	Revenue Deductions	$-	$-	$-	$-	$-	$-
20							
21	Net Revenues	$-	$-	$-	$-	$-	$-
22							
23	**Expenses:**						
24	Hospital Salaries	$360,959	$342,911	$(18,048)	$2,598,904	$2,743,288	$144,384
25	Contract labor	$-	$-	$-	$14,378	$-	$(14,378)
26	Benefits	$-	$-	$-	$-	$-	$-
27	Supplies	$86,630	$80,685	$(5,945)	$532,690	$645,479	$112,789
28	Maintenance and Repairs	$-	$-	$-	$-	$-	$-
29	Outside Services	$132,705	$100,856	$(31,849)	$1,061,644	$806,849	$(254,795)
30	Rental Expense	$-	$-	$-	$-	$-	$-
31	Depreciation	$-	$-	$-	$-	$-	$-
32	Interest	$-	$-	$-	$-	$-	$-
33	Property Taxes	$-	$-	$-	$-	$-	$-
34	Insurance	$-	$-	$-	$-	$-	$-
35	Other Expenses	$-	$5,000	$5,000	$-	$5,000	$5,000
36	Total Expenses	$580,295	$529,452	$(50,842)	$4,207,616	$4,200,616	$(7,000)
37							
38	**Net Margin**	$(580,295)	$(529,452)	$(50,842)	$(4,207,616)	$(4,200,616)	$(7,000)

departmental stat changes, and for the overhead department, notice there are no revenues.

Now look at **Exhibit 31**. Here I have taken a shot at "trueing-up" **Exhibit 28** *(page 174)* to reflect everything associated with the department. You will never see a department income statement that looks like this. I only show it here to drive home one point: Do *not* believe that your department is making as much money as it appears when you look at your departmental income statement! As you can see here, the picture changes dramatically when you "fill in the blanks." Compare the two Exhibits. In **Exhibit 28** and **Exhibit 31**, volumes and Gross Revenues are the same. The expenses shown in **Exhibit 28** are the same in **Exhibit 31**. The difference is the addition of Revenue Deductions and expenses that the department incurs but are not charged to them. In **Exhibit 28**, the department missed budget for the month by $31,728 but was solidly ahead of budget on a year-to-date basis (up by $624,587). But in **Exhibit 31**, the department missed budget for the month by $91,307, *and* is behind on a year-to-date basis as well, by $387,327.

In my example, the shift in the year-to-date variance is caused by revenue deductions as a percent of revenues on a year-to-date basis being much higher than budget. This can be caused by many things, all beyond the scope of this book. You just need to know that gross revenues being ahead of budget does *not* always mean that net revenue will be, too! That is important to remember.

MONTHLY OPERATING REVIEW (MOR)

When you hear someone talk about MORs, they may be talking about either a report or an event. The *event* is simply the meeting to discuss the *report*. If finance-ese is a foreign language for people in hospital operations, an MOR report is a sort of finance-to-operations translation dictionary.

The content and appearance of the report will vary greatly. And both the report and the event may (and should) cover more than finances. It will probably also cover at least quality issues and patient satisfaction and may cover other things, as well. But since this book is only about finance, that is the only part of the MOR that we will consider.

This chapter will look at how to read the report, and a later chapter will cover preparing for—and actually participating in—the event.

Look at **Exhibit 32** *(page 180)*. This is an example of the finance portion of an MOR. What your organization chooses to include on it and how it is presented will vary greatly. I have included more items than usual, so I would guess that your MOR will contain less information. The reason I've included everything that I *did* is to be able to better help you understand how some of the numbers are calculated and why they are important. I did limit my presentation to just the current month, whereas many hospitals will also include a section showing YTD. I limited my example for simplicity purposes. The

	EXHIBIT 31						
1	J Lee Community Hospital						
2	Radiology Department						
3	Fiscal year 2011						
4	Month ending May 31, 2011						
5							
6	Column	A	B	C	D	E	F
7		Current Month			Year to Date		
8		Actual	Budget	Variance	Actual	Budget	Variance
9	**Dept Stat - Exams:**						
10	Inpatient Exams	3,348	3,100	248	21,427	24,300	(2,873)
11	Outpatient Exams	3,949	4,030	(81)	37,914	31,590	6,324
12	Total Exams	7,297	7,130	167	59,341	55,890	3,451
13							
14	**Revenues:**						
15	Gross Inpatient revenues	$1,432,944	$1,240,000	$192,944	$8,785,152	$9,720,000	$(934,848)
16	Gross Outpatient revenues	$1,382,290	$1,612,000	$(229,710)	$14,407,411	$12,636,000	$1,771,411
17	Total Gross Revenues	$2,815,234	$2,852,000	$(36,766)	$23,192,563	$22,356,000	$836,563
18							
19	Revenue Deductions	$1,829,902	$1,768,240	$(61,662)	$14,843,240	$13,860,720	$(982,520)
20							
21	Net Revenues	$985,332	$1,083,760	$(98,428)	$8,349,323	$8,495,280	$(145,957)
22							
23	**Expenses:**						
24	Hospital Salaries	$198,433	$205,629	$7,196	$1,739,891	$1,588,104	$(151,787)
25	Contract labor	$15,987	$-	$(15,987)	$72,397	$-	$(72,397)
26	Benefits	$43,655	$45,238	$1,583	$382,776	$349,383	$(33,393)
27	Supplies	$20,693	$19,821	$(871)	$161,670	$155,374	$(6,296)
28	Maintenance and Repairs	$1,500	$12,000	$10,500	$82,356	$96,000	$13,644
29	Outside Services	$-	$3,200	$3,200	$21,741	$25,600	$3,859
30	Rental Expense	$-	$-	$-	$-	$-	$-
31	Depreciation	$5,000	$5,000	$-	$40,000	$40,000	$-
32	Interest	$2,000	$2,500	$500	$16,000	$20,000	$4,000
33	Property Taxes	$100	$100	$-	$800	$800	$-
34	Insurance	$1,000	$1,000	$-	$8,000	$8,000	$-
35	Other Expenses	$500	$1,500	$1,000	$11,000	$12,000	$1,000
36	Total Expenses	$288,868	$295,989	$7,121	$2,536,630	$2,295,261	$(241,369)
37							
38	**Net Margin**	$696,464	$787,771	$(91,307)	$5,812,692	$6,200,019	$(387,327)

	EXHIBIT 32					
	Monthly Operating Review					
	Department: Surgical Nursing Unit					
	Month: May 2011					
		A	B	C	D	E	F
		Current Month					
		Actual	Budget	Volume Adjusted Budget	Variance to Budget	Variance to Vol Adj Budget	Impact Against Vol Adj Budget
1	**I. VOLUME**						
2	Patient Days	1,333	1,488	N/A	(155)	N/A	N/A
3	Equivalent Observation days	155	124	N/A	31	N/A	N/A
4	Total Units of Service	1,488	1,612	N/A	(124)	N/A	N/A
5	Average Daily Census	48	52	N/A	(4)	N/A	N/A
6	Occupancy Rate	80%	87%	N/A	-7%	N/A	N/A
7	**II. LABOR MANAGEMENT**						
8	Productivity:						
9	Employed worked Nursing Hours per UOS	7.25	5.10	5.10	(2.15)	(2.15)	N/A
10	Contract Labor Worked Hours per UOS	0.25	-	-	(0.25)	(0.25)	N/A
11	Other Worked Hours per UOS	1.75	3.50	3.50	1.75	1.75	N/A
12	Total Worked Hours per UOS	9.25	8.60	8.60	(0.65)	(0.65)	N/A
13	Non-Prod Hours per UOS	0.99	0.86	0.86	(0.13)	(0.13)	N/A
14	Total Paid Hours per UOS	10.24	9.46	9.46	(0.78)	(0.78)	N/A
15	FTEs:						
16	Employed worked Nursing FTEs	61.07	46.54	42.96	(14.53)	(18.11)	N/A
17	Contract Labor FTEs	2.11	0.00	0.00	(2.11)	(2.11)	N/A
18	Other worked FTEs	14.74	31.94	29.48	17.20	14.74	N/A
19	Total worked FTEs	77.91	78.48	72.44	0.56	(5.48)	N/A
20	Non-Prod FTEs	8.34	7.85	7.24	(0.49)	(1.10)	N/A
21	Total Paid FTEs	86.25	86.32	79.68	0.07	(6.57)	N/A
22	Rate:						
23	Average Hourly Rate - Payroll	$32.00	$31.50	$31.15	$(0.50)	$(0.85)	N/A
24	Average Hourly Rate - Contract	$55.00	$-	$-	$(55.00)	$(55.00)	N/A
25	Total AHR	$32.56	$31.50	$31.15	$(1.06)	$(1.41)	N/A
26							
27	Premium Hours (OT+CL+CB)	814	347	-	(467)	(814)	N/A
28	Premium Hours as Percentage of Worked Hours	5.91%	2.50%	0.00%	-3.41%	-5.91%	N/A
29	**III. EXPENSES**						
30	Employed Cost per UOS	$319.68	$297.99	$294.68	$(21.69)	$(25.00)	$(37,201)
31	Contract Labor Cost per UOS	$13.75	$-	$-	$(13.75)	$(13.75)	$(20,460)
32	Total Paid Labor Cost per UOS	$333.43	$297.99	$294.68	$(35.44)	$(38.75)	$(57,661)
33	Supply costs per UOS	$1.53	$1.50	$1.50	$(0.03)	$(0.03)	$(45)
34	Other Expenses per UOS	$3.24	$3.61	$3.61	$0.37	$0.37	$544
35	Total Cost per UOS	$336.67	$301.60	$299.79	$(35.07)	$(36.89)	$(54,886)

year-to-date concepts are exactly the same. We will aim for understanding what story the MOR tells in the next chapter. The purpose of showing it to you here is just so you can see what an MOR looks like, and how it is different from a Departmental Income Statement. All of the information presented here is derived from the hospital accounting system. Some of you may see some or all of it included on your Departmental Income Statement. It doesn't matter where you see it, or how it is presented. The formulas are the same.

I will use this same MOR in the next chapter to talk about the story it tells.

Looking at the title, you can see that it refers to the Surgical Nursing unit for the month of May, 2011.

If you look back at **Exhibit 29** *(page 176)*, you will notice that it is a departmental income statement for the same department for the same month.

Comparing **Exhibit 29** with **Exhibit 32**, you will notice that other than volume indicators, you don't see any of the numbers from the departmental income statement on the MOR, or vice versa. The two reports are closely related in that the data behind the numbers is much the same, but *the purpose of the MOR is to help tell the story*. Assuming you know what happened in your department during the month, the MOR helps connect the dots and shows how variances between budgeted and actual activities affected the financial results.

Let's look briefly at how the MOR I've presented is laid out, and what the purpose of each section is.

When you look at **Exhibit 32**, you notice there are three sections: Volume, Labor Management, and Expenses.

I. VOLUME

The volume section has three columns. All three of these columns are the same ones shown in **Exhibit 29** *(page 176)*. *Rows 2, 3, and 4* come straight from the departmental income statement. *Row 5* is the ADC. See **Chapter 1** if you don't recall what ADC is or how it's calculated. *Row 6* is the departmental occupancy rate. The formula is the ADC / total available beds in the unit. It is an indicator of how "full" the unit is. In this example, the ADC is 48. the unit must have 60 beds (a number not shown here). So if the census averages 48 out of a 60 bed unit, that is 80% occupied (48/60 = 80%).

Why does an MOR include volume indicators? As we've discussed many times before, volume drives resource utilization. In revenue-generating departments, volume drives revenue. Even in many non-revenue generating departments, volume also loosely drives revenue. For example, Admitting is not a revenue-generating department, but the statistic for the department is registrations. If registrations for the department are higher than budget, then gross revenue for the hospital probably is, too.

II. LABOR MANAGEMENT

It always seems to keep coming back to labor management, doesn't it? Why does an MOR include labor management indicators? I'm hoping that by now, you know the answer to that question. Does 50% of operating expenses ring a bell?

Labor Management is divided into three sections and each section has five columns. Let's go over the columns first. I'll assume you understand the Actual and Budget columns *(columns A and B)*. Column C is labeled "Volume Adjusted Budget." The data in this column has been calculated to show what the budget would have been if you had been able to see into a crystal ball, and had budgeted using the EXACT volume you actually experienced *(if that sentence seemed confusing, you may want to re-read it: this is an important concept that we will come back to again and again)*. In some instances, the data is the same as Budget *(column B)*, and in some instances it is different. This will perhaps become more understood as we go over the formulas for each row. *Column D* is titled "Variance to Budget," and is simply the difference between *column A* and *column B*. *Column E* is titled "Variance to Volume Adjusted Budget" and is the difference between *column A* and *column C*.

Let's look at the sections and rows:

Productivity

Row 9: Employed worked nursing hours per UOS. The formula for this row is worked nursing hours divided by the department stat or "UOS" (units of service). Many hospitals like to track and monitor nursing hours separate from other skill levels. If your department does not have nurses in it, this row will be blank (or may not even be on your MOR). The hours behind this indicator are not shown on the report. They most likely come out of either the payroll or accounting system. Notice that columns B and C are the same. In this instance, it doesn't matter whether the actual volume was different than the budgeted volume since this number is already "volume adjusted." It is a "per stat" number.

Side-bar note to Nursing units: I hope I don't confuse you when I say this generally does not apply to "volume adjusting" for Nursing units. Remember in **Chapter 13** we discussed how Nursing units are less productive when they have a lower census? We looked at **Exhibit 10** *(page 77)* and saw how productivity is worse when volume is lower? If you're reading this paragraph and thinking, "Yay! The MOR will adjust the productivity stat for me when my volume is different than budget," my first inclination is to be happy that you have grasped these concepts. Sadly though, I must report that in terms of an automated report, this adjustment will likely not happen.

The budgeted MH/stat in *column B* and the volume adjusted budgeted MH/stat in *column C* will be the same. You will have to manually figure out what the volume-adjusted budgeted MH/stat needs to be. This column works well for wholly variable departments, but not as well for semi-variable departments.

Row 10: Contract labor hours per UOS. The formula for this row is contract labor hours divided by the department stat or UOS. The hours behind this indicator are not shown on this report. Because it is contract labor, the information probably comes from some type of tracking system used by the hospital to track contract labor. Again notice that *columns B and C* are the same for the same reason as *row 9*.

Row 11: Other worked hours per UOS. The formula for this row is all non-nursing employed worked hours in the department divided by the department stat or UOS. In a Nursing unit, it would include positions such as unit secretaries or patient care assistants. In non-Nursing units, all employed, worked hours may be on this row. The hours for this indicator are not shown on this report. They most likely come out of either the payroll or accounting system. Again notice that columns B and C are the same for the same reason as *row 9*.

Row 12: Total worked hours per UOS. The formula for this row is the sum of *rows 9, 10 and 11*. Many MORs show only this row instead of showing the detail. But as you will see in the next chapter, when you are trying to explain variances, it is very helpful to have this detail.

Row 13: Non-Prod hours per UOS. The formula for this row is total non-productive hours divided by the units of service. As discussed earlier (in **Chapters 8** and **13**), non-productive hours are those hours that are paid by the company for time spent doing tasks that did not result in a statistic being generated. Examples are vacation and sick time, education seminars covered by the hospital, and perhaps orientation time. The hours for this indicator are not shown on this report. They most likely come out of either the payroll or accounting system. Again notice that *columns B and C* are the same for the same reason as *row 9*.

Row 14: Total Paid hours per UOS. The formula for this row is the sum of row 12 and row 13. For some hospitals, this is the only productivity stat shown. I do not care for this approach. If this is the only data provided, it is virtually impossible to know where to begin to explain a variance, since the variance can come from things that happened on *rows 9, 10, 11 or 13*. Again notice that *columns B and C* are the same for the same reason as *row 9*.

FTEs

Rows 16 through 21 are the same as rows 9 through 14, except instead of "per UOS" it shows the FTEs themselves. Mathematically, the two sections are related. The Productivity section takes hours and divides them by units of service. The FTEs section takes the exact same hours and divides them by the number of hours per FTE. The month shown is May, which has 31 days. So, as discussed in **Chapter 1**, in May, 1 FTE = (2,080/365 x 31) = 176.66 hours.

Notice that in this section *column C* is different than *column B*. Now perhaps it will be easier to understand what I was trying to explain earlier.

Remember from the Volume section that budgeted units of service were 1,612 *(row 4 column B)*, and actual units of service were only 1,488 (row 4 column A). Remember also, from the Productivity section, that the budgeted employed, worked nursing hours per UOS *(row 9 column B)* were 5.1. Putting that together, *column C* shows that if you had known when you prepared the budget that you should budget 1,488 UOS, and budgeted productivity was the same at 5.1, then only 42.96 FTEs would have been budgeted.

Said another way, *Column C* applies **budgeted** *productivity to* **actual** *volume*. Now look at *row 21*. You see that actual FTEs *(column A)* were 86.25 on a budget of 86.32. Seems like you did pretty well, huh? But wait. Since volume was less than budget, revenue will be, too. So FTEs should be, as well. How much less? That is what *column C* shows. According to *column C*, with volume of 1,488, FTEs should have only been 79.68. Instead of being almost exactly on target *(row 21 column D)*, FTEs were actually over by 6.57 *(row 21 column E)* when you adjust the FTE budget to actual volumes x the budgeted MH/stat. We'll discuss why and what caused this in the next chapter. Right now, you only need to understand the concept of a volume-adjusted budget.

Rate

The Rate section of the MOR looks at rates of pay and premium pay. Why are pay rates and premium pay indicators included in the MOR? Think about your own paycheck. Setting aside things like shift differentials, call pay, etc., how much you get paid is a formula:

Hours Worked x Rate per Hour

If you want to increase (or decrease) your paycheck, you can change either the number of hours you work or the rate you are paid per hour. It works exactly the same way for a hospital's labor costs.

Productivity focuses on the first half of the equation: number of hours worked. The average hourly rate ("AHR") focuses on the second half: rate per hour. AHR is the overall blended rate of all the people paid during the period. It is a weighted average and moves up when more higher-dollar hours are worked, and moves down when more lower-dollar hours are worked. As we discussed in Chapter 13, the rate changes every time the mix of higher paid staff and lower paid staff hours shifts. If a Nursing unit uses unit secretaries (paid at a rate lower than nurses) to do some of the work in the department, it will drive down the AHR in the department, compared to the same Nursing unit that uses more nurses and no unit secretaries. Comparing the AHR to budget gives an indication as to whether the skill mix that was budgeted is close to the skill mix actually being used. It can also indicate whether or not too much overtime is being used.

Remember when we were looking at productivity (hours worked) in **Chapter 13**, we discussed how an extra 30 minutes per patient day could add up to hours that would cost a hospital with a census of 500 an extra 5.2 million dollars? Rate can have just as large of an impact. A hospital or hospital system with 5,000 FTEs would also spend an extra $5.2 million a year paying everyone an extra fifty cents per hour (5,000 FTEs x 2,080 hours per year x $.50 = $5.2 million)! So 30 extra minutes plus 50 cents per hour can add up to **$10.4 million per year!** That's almost *a million dollars a month!*

Rows 23, 24, and 25 show the actual and budgeted AHR for hospital employees, contract labor and the blended rate of the two. Remember, the overall AHR is a *blend* of the employed and contact rates. Since there are usually many more employed hours than contract hours, the blended rate is usually much closer to the employed rate. Look at *Column C on rows 23 and 25.* Notice it is different than the budget. I'll talk more about why in a minute.

Rows 27 and 28 show the hours and percentage of total hours of premium labor hours. Remember, in **Chapter 13** we discussed premium labor. Premium labor is any labor that there is an "added" or "premium" cost per hour. There are three types of premium labor: contract labor, overtime, and callback pay. You can see that in our example, 814 hours of premium labor were used. The budget was 347, and the budget assumed 1,612 units of service, and there were only 1,488. Are you starting to get an inkling of why the Volume Adjusted Budget shows zero premium labor (row 27 column C), and the Volume Adjusted Budgeted AHR is lower than budget?

Maybe the dots haven't started to connect for you yet.

Go back up to *row 14 columns B and C.* They show a budget of 9.46 hours per UOS. The budget assumed 1,612 UOS:

1,612 UOS x 9.46 hrs per UOS = 15,250 hours

But the actual UOS were only 1,488. Applying the budgeted hours per UOS:

1,488 UOS x 9.46 hrs per UOS = 12,588 hours

So in a perfect world, you would have spent 2,662 *fewer* hours caring for patients (15,250—12,588). And (also in a perfect world), the very first hours you would eliminate would be the premium hours. Since the number of premium hours budgeted was 347, all of those hours should have been able to be eliminated.

I know. I know. I can hear you now. "That's easy for you to say and show on paper. It's not that easy or simple." I do know that. The purpose of calculating it this way on the MOR is to prompt you to think about that when you are making decisions, and to prompt the conversation during the MOR meeting about what obstacles there were for you to not be able to eliminate premium labor when volumes were under budget. And by the way, this is also the reason that *rows 23 and 25, column C* are less than the budget. Remember the $31.50 shown in *column B line 23* includes those 347 hours of overtime. So if those overtime hours are eliminated, the AHR will drop. We accountants like it when everything fits together!

Let's look now at the last section of the MOR.

III. EXPENSES

This section is where it all comes together. In Sections I and II we looked at volumes against budget, and looked at labor productivity and rates against both budget and a volume adjusted budget. In this Section, the financial impact of these variances are pulled together.

Rows 30, 31 and 32 are all related to labor. (Yup—back to that again!) Here we see what happens when you combine the impact of variances in the number of hours per patient, and the average rate. The formula for calculating the cost per UOS is simple:

Total costs *divided by* units of service

For *row 30 column A* then, the math is total actual hospital salary expense divided by the actual UOS. Go back to **Exhibit 29** *(page 176)*. See the $475,684 salary cost in *column A row 24* of that Exhibit? And remember the actual UOS were 1,488 (shown on *row 12 column A of Exhibit 29*).

$475,684 *divided by* 1,488 = $319.68

So the actual cost per UOS was $319.68, which is shown on *row 30 column A* of **Exhibit 32**. The same formula applies to *column B*. You can't see the numbers behind *column C*, but the number shown is what the cost would have been per UOS without any premium labor (as discussed above).

You can see when you look at *column A* (actual) that the cost of spending more hours per UOS AND doing it at a higher AHR combined to generate a cost per UOS that is $35.44 higher than the budget *(column D)*. $35.44 is 12% over budget. Not Good. And even worse is that it is $38.75 higher than the volume adjusted budget *(column E)*. 13% over the volume-adjusted budget. So should we be concerned? How big is a 13% variance? We'll come back to that in a few minutes. Let's finish looking at the remaining rows in Section III first.

Three rows are left in section III. The formulas and concepts are the same as we have already discussed. The actual *(column A)* supply cost per UOS can be validated by looking back at **Exhibit 29**:

Supply costs of $2,277 (row 27 column A)
***divided by* UOS of 1,488 = $1.53**

The budgeted supply cost per UOS can be validated the same way:

Supply cost budget, $2,418 (row 27 column B) / budgeted UOS of 1,612 = $1.50

Notice again that the volume adjusted budget is the same as the budget for the same reason that the two numbers are the same in the hours per UOS discussion: the number is already volume-adjusted.

The exercise above can be repeated for *row 34*. *Row 34* includes *all remaining expenses*—not *just* the expense line named "Other expenses." For this department that includes (looking back at **Exhibit 29** again) "rental expense" and "Other expenses." Looking back at **Exhibit 32** *(page 180)*, you can see that in this case, the actual expense per UOS *(row 34 column A)* is less than the budget.

I presented Other expenses this way because this is how many hospitals do it. But I don't want to confuse you. When we discussed budgeting and monitoring these expenses, we talked about them being fixed. Fixed, as in, they are not impacted by changes in volume like salaries and supplies can be. They typically will not be reduced just because volume is less—unless you intervene and do something to suppress them. We talked about that in earlier chapters.

So why would hospitals look at them this way on the MOR? Remember the discussions we have had about revenue being volume driven? In an ideal world, if your department has less volume than budgeted, you will try to find ways to reduce fixed expenses. So although the reduced volume does not impact them, perhaps your actions can reduce them low enough that their cost per UOS can match budget. If your volume is lower than budget, and you do NOT intervene to lower your fixed costs, then the cost per UOS will be over (unfavorable to) budget. And if volume is less, then chances are revenue will be less. Less revenue without reduced expenses will mean you do not achieve your budgeted bottom line.

I have always remembered one of the first lessons I learned when I started in accounting. Having one line item significantly over budget on a percentage basis may not mean it is material in the grand scheme of things. For example, let's say you have an item budgeted at $1,000 and it ends up costing $3,000. The variance is 200%, but if your total budget is $1 million, the $2,000 variance is still immaterial. So keeping that in mind, let's look at the variances shown on **Exhibit 32**, Section III again, and decide whether or not they are material.

Notice that Section III has an extra column on the far right (column F). "Impact Against Volume Adjusted Budget." This is the final piece of the puzzle. Your MOR may or may not include this information. But I think it is important that you know and understand this concept.

The math to calculate the numbers shown in *column F* is simple. For all rows in Section III, the amount shown in *column E* is multiplied by the actual volume for the month (1,488 UOS). For example, look at *row 30, column E*. It says that the cost per UOS variance against the volume adjusted budget is $25.00.

Seems like a mouthful, huh? Ok, let me say it another way. The $25.00 variance per UOS is the difference between what you *should have spent* per unit of service, and what you *did* spend per UOS. If you had 1,488 units of service, and spent an extra $25 on each one, then you spent an extra.

$$\$25.00 \times 1,488 = \$37,201$$

Look at *column F on row 30*, and you will see the $37,201. The same exercise is repeated for *rows 31, 33, and 34. Row 32* is the sum of *rows 31 and 32, and row 35* is the sum of *rows 32, 33, and 34.*

So what do these numbers say? *Row 32 column F* says that in total, the excess number of hours, coupled with the excess overtime and contract labor (premium labor) ended up costing an extra $57,661. In the case of supplies, the extra $.03 only cost an extra $45, and fixed expenses were actually under by $544. So in total, the financial performance of the department was $54,886 worse than it should have been.

"But Wait!" you say. "When I look at **Exhibit 29** *(page 176)*, it only shows that my expenses were $14,793 over budget. Why don't the two numbers tie?"

Aha! Good question! Why don't the two numbers tie? They don't tie because volume was different. Because volume was less than budget, expenses should have been less than budget. And they were more than budget. The spread between what they should have been given the reduced volume and what they were is the $54,886.

So that is what an MOR looks like.

Ready to pull it all together?

Chapter 17 Self Review Questions

1. Name the two most common reports you will use to perform month end review.

2. What does MOR stand for, and what is it?

3. What is the difference between **Exhibit 28** and **Exhibit 31**?

4. Which one is a truer reflection of the department manager's performance—**Exhibit 28** or **Exhibit 31**?

5. How does an MOR relate to the Departmental Income Statement?

Seven Questions

Take a deep breath! You've made it to the end. Here we are, getting ready to apply everything you've learned so far. If you understand everything in this book up to now, then this chapter will be pretty easy. We're going to walk through the preparation I recommend you do to review your departmental financial performance, while you are simultaneously preparing for your MOR (the event).

I keep talking about finance being a language. Well, throughout this book you have learned the language. Or maybe I should say you have learned many many words. In this chapter, we will put those words together and speak!

Let's start with an overview of the process that I recommend everyone follow—regardless of your department. After that, I'll walk through a review of each of the three types of departments: Nursing, Ancillary, and an overhead department. We will use the department financial statements that you saw in the last chapter.

OVERVIEW

My recommendation to you would be to develop your own organized approach to reviewing your financial statements. Make it a process that works for you. I recommend you include the following key steps:

A. **Block time on your calendar to do this.** Have it be a standing appointment you have with yourself. Time when you can close your door and focus.

B. **Gather everything you need to perform the review.** You will need more than your department financial statements and your MOR (report). Here are some things you may want:

1. A month end productivity report if your company produces one

2. Your copy of your budget

3. Your copy of your staffing matrix, or schedule

4. Notes you may have accumulated to yourself about large unusual expenses that occurred during the month

5. Logs or notes to yourself on when and why premium labor was used (contract, overtime or callback): sitter logs, notes on vacancies, turnover, employees being out for FMLA, etc.

6. Financial statements from last month, and perhaps from the same month last year if your departments are very seasonally influenced (your departmental financial statements may already show some or all of this information for you)

C. **Review the financials in conjunction with all the other data you have around you.** You will know you are finished when you can tell your story for the month. Being able to tell your story for the month means being able to answer the following seven questions:

1. Are the financials correct? If not, did you report the errors?

2. What are the unfavorable variances? Here, I define a variance as a difference in the cost per UOS for labor and supplies, and a pure dollar variance for all other (fixed) expenses.

3. Why did they occur?

4. Have the events that caused them been corrected?

5. If not, why not, and when will they be corrected?

6. What help do you need to correct them?

7. How are you doing this month?

Block time. Gather data. Perform the review. Three steps. Seven simple questions. OK, maybe not so simple sometimes. But this process isn't meant to be scary. If you are an engaged manager, and know what is happening in your department each day, you will know the answers to these questions. So let's get started. We'll take them one department at a time and find the answers to The Seven Questions.

ADMITTING

Look at **Exhibit 33** and look back at **Exhibit 30** *(page 177)*. **Exhibit 33** is the MOR that goes with the Admitting department financial statement in **Exhibit 30**. Let's review! Remember to keep The Seven Questions in mind as you review.

1. Before we even start reviewing, we need to set the stage. If this was your department, and you had been doing all the "monthly monitoring" outlined in previous chapters, you should be able to close your eyes and think about what you know. Think about your story. At the very least, you should know:

		A	B	C	D	E	F
	EXHIBIT 33						
	Monthly Operating Review						
	Department: Admitting						
	Month: May 2011						
		A	B	C	D	E	F
		Current Month					
		Actual	Budget	Volume Adjusted Budget	Variance to Budget	Variance to Vol Adj Budget	Impact Against Vol Adj Budget
1	**I. VOLUME**						
2	Registrations	42,466	40,342	N/A	2,123	N/A	N/A
3							
4	Total Units of Service	42,466	40,342	N/A	2,123	N/A	N/A
5							
6							
7	**II. LABOR MANAGEMENT**						
8	Productivity:						
9	Employed worked Nursing Hours per UOS			-	-	-	N/A
10	Contract Labor Worked Hours per UOS		-	-	-	-	N/A
11	Other Worked Hours per UOS	0.52	0.49	0.49	(0.03)	(0.03)	N/A
12	Total Worked Hours per UOS	0.52	0.49	0.49	(0.03)	(0.03)	N/A
13	Non-Prod Hours per UOS	0.04	0.05	0.05	0.02	0.02	N/A
14	Total Paid Hours per UOS	0.56	0.55	0.55	(0.02)	(0.02)	N/A
15	FTEs:						
16	Employed worked Nursing FTEs	0.00	0.00	0.00	0.00	0.00	N/A
17	Contract Labor FTEs	0.00	0.00	0.00	0.00	0.00	N/A
18	Other worked FTEs	125.68	112.13	118.03	(13.55)	(7.64)	N/A
19	Total worked FTEs	125.68	112.13	118.03	(13.55)	(7.64)	N/A
20	Non-Prod FTEs	9.46	12.46	13.11	3.00	3.66	N/A
21	Total Paid FTEs	135.13	124.59	131.15	(10.55)	(3.99)	N/A
22	Rate:						
23	Average Hourly Rate - Payroll	$15.12	$15.58	$15.58	$0.46	$0.46	N/A
24	Average Hourly Rate - Contract	$-	$-	$-	$-	$-	N/A
25	Total AHR	$15.12	$15.58	$15.58	$0.46	$0.46	N/A
26							
27	Premium Hours (OT+CL+CB)	764	440	463	(324)	(301)	N/A
28	Premium Hours as Percentage of Worked Hours	3.20%	2.00%	2.00%	-1.20%	-1.20%	N/A
29	**III. EXPENSES**						
30	Employed Cost per UOS	$8.50	$8.50	$8.50	$-	$-	$-
31	Contract Labor Cost per UOS	$-	$-	$-	$-	$-	$-
32	Total Paid Labor Cost per UOS	$8.50	$8.50	$8.50	$-	$-	$-
33	Supply costs per UOS	$2.04	$2.00	$2.00	$(0.04)	$(0.04)	$(1,699)
34	Other Expenses per UOS	$3.13	$2.62	$2.62	$(0.50)	$(0.50)	$(21,278)
35	Total Cost per UOS	$13.67	$13.12	$13.12	$(0.54)	$(0.54)	$(22,977)

- This is May, 2011. The eighth month of the hospital's fiscal year (which ends on September 30, 2011).

- Based on the daily stat reports you saw, volume was over budget.

- Based on the productivity reports you reviewed, you think you did a decent job managing labor. Paid MH/Stat was very close to budget, and in previous months the average hourly rate has been under budget a bit, so you think your cost per UOS should be OK.

- You do not recall having any unusual expenses occur or come to you for approval.

2. With this information in mind, look first at the department financial statement. Start at the top of the page and move down it. Volume first. It does show it is over budget (that's a good thing!) by about 5% *(row 12 column C* shows an extra 2,123 registrations on a budget of 40,342). The 42,466 registrations shown on *row 4 column A* appears reasonable to you based on what you knew about volume going through the month.

3. Based on the higher-than-budget volume, you are not initially surprised to see that salaries are over budget *(row 24)*. You don't have enough information here to know if the excess expense was driven by the higher volume or if something else happened. You need to see the MOR to determine that. When you look at the MOR, first look at *row 32*. Your cost per registration was right on budget at $8.50. For me—that is all that really matters. That is the end goal. If you look at the Labor Management section of the MOR, there are some unfavorable variances: *Row 12* shows worked hours per registration were over budget, *row 14* shows paid hours per registration were over budget, and *rows 27 and 28* show use of overtime was over budget. but....row 23 shows the average hourly rate was $.46 less than budget. This one favorable variance compensated for all of the unfavorable variances. You have nothing to apologize for.

4. Supply expense is over budget, too. But again, because of the higher than budgeted volume, you think this might be OK. But you don't have the information to know for sure. Look at the MOR. Go to *row 33*. It shows the cost per unit of service to be $2.04 on a budget of $2.00. Applying that $.04 unfavorable variance to the actual volume for the month indicates that you overspent by $1,699 *(row 33 column F)*. Confused? If so, you may want to revisit **Chapter 17** to understand the difference between the $1,699 variance shown on the MOR *(***Exhibit 33,** *page 193 row 33 column F)* and the $5,945 variance shown on the department financial *(***Exhibit 30,** *page 177, row 27 column C)*. The MOR **(Exhibit 33,** *page 193)* shows the budget was $2.00 per registration *(row 33 column B)*. Actual registrations were 42,466. If you had stayed within

the $2.00 per registration, you would have spent $2.00 x 42,466 = $84,932. If you had only spent $84,931, then you would have been over the budget of $80,685 *(row 27 column B on* **Exhibit 30***)* by $4,246 ($84,931 - $80,685). But you were over by $5,945 *(row 27 column C).* The difference between the amount you should have been over ($4,246) and the amount you WERE over ($5,945) is $1,699. That is the amount shown on the MOR *(***Exhibit 33***, page 193, row 33 column F).* If you followed all that, then what it says is that even though you were over budget by $5,945 *(***Exhibit 30***, page 177, row 27 column C),* your true unexplained variance is only $1,699 *(***Exhibit 33***, page 193, row 33 column F).* On a cost per registration, you are only over budget by $.04, which is 2% of the budgeted $2.00 per registration. Using my 5% threshold, this is probably too small of a variance to investigate. But for educational purposes, let's assume you do need to investigate it. Where would you start?

- The first thing I would do, is to see how I was doing on a YTD basis. If the cost per registration on a YTD basis is under budget, then this month may have just been caused by an order placed late in the month, and I expect those goods to be used the following month (which will reduce orders and expense next month). If the YTD amount per registration is over budget, then perhaps there is a recurring problem that needs to be addressed. And maybe it already has. Maybe it is because a new form has been introduced in to the department that wasn't budgeted for, and it is putting that expense over budget every month. So how do you look on a YTD basis for supplies per registration? Hmm . . . don't see that number anywhere? Not on the financial statement, and not on the MOR. Don't worry—you know how to calculate it! Look at **Exhibit 30**, *page 177, row 27 column D and row 12 column D.* Divide *row 27* by *row 12*: $532,690 / 271,781 = $1.96. So your YTD supply cost per registration is $1.96. Now repeat the exercise for *row 27 column E* and *row 12 column E*: $645,479 / 322,740 = $2.00. The budgeted YTD cost per registration is $2.00 and you have spent only $1.96. You are under budget. That may be all you need to say in your MOR. But what if you wanted to investigate the overage for the month anyway?

- Going back to **Chapter 3** and the Trial Balance, you would probably want to get a copy of the section for supply expenses for your department for the current month. That detail may be provided to you already. Remember the trial balance will show you all the supply accounts. Hopefully you will be able to zero in on what account is over budget. Using our example from above, you would expect to see that the forms account was over budget.

5. Outside Services is over budget by $31,849, which is 32%. With no additional information, this would be very concerning. If I were you, I would wonder if there was a mistake. However, notice that the year-to-date amount *(row 29 column F)* is over budget by 32% as well. In fact, the YTD variance *(row 29 column F)* is close to being exactly equal to eight times the monthly variance (remember, the hospital has a September 30 year end, so May YTD reflects eight months of activity). This means this variance has probably been occurring every month since the year began. Which means you and the CFO would probably already know what causes it every month. Unless there is something you were supposed to have been doing about this variance, there is probably nothing else to do. For purposes of this discussion, let's say it relates to unbudgeted outsourced collection fees.

6. Look at *row 35*. The actual expense for the month and for the YTD are both $0, while the budget is $5,000 (for the month and YTD). This means that something was budgeted to happen in May that cost $5,000 that had never happened before (nor was it budgeted to happen). Usually that would be something like an annual inspection and license fee or an annual seminar. Why doesn't any expense show here? There are two options. First, there is a mistake on the financial statements. Perhaps finance accidentally charged the expense to the wrong department. Or perhaps the inspection occurred, but the bill has not yet been received. The second option is that the expense did not occur. Perhaps it was a seminar, and because of the extra outside services expenses you are incurring, it was decided not to attend the budgeted seminar. Only you know the answer. If there was a mistake, you need to notify the appropriate person in finance. Using the inspection example, if the inspection occurred, but the bill has not been received, you need to notify finance so they can accrue the expenses (see **Chapter 16** for a refresher on the hows and whys of accruals). For purposes of this review, let's say that upon investigation you found the money budgeted was to cover an inspection. The inspection did not occur—it is expected to occur next month instead.

7. When you closed your eyes and thought about what you expected to see, was there anything that came to mind that you do not see? Regardless of whether or not it was budgeted, were there any expenses that you do not see here? Perhaps you had a repair. There is nothing on the department financial. So if that occurred, you would need to notify finance so they could accrue it. I think this is perhaps the *biggest* mistake folks make when they review financial statements. They only review for what is there. They forget to review for what isn't there. Or maybe they don't forget. Maybe they like it better when their expenses show as being less than they actually were. Even if they are wrong. I can tell you my

preference. When I was growing up, my Dad used to tell me if I screwed up, I would be in twice as much trouble if I lied about it. I guess maybe I apply that here. If you have an expense that wasn't reported, I will be much more upset when it comes through in a future month than if you report it now. The CFO is making future decisions based on what is showing on the financial statements NOW. If there are expenses missing, then that means the hospital's bottom line is less than what is showing. You may think that maybe just one small expense in your department can't make that much difference. But what if every department head thought that way? It adds up quickly. Also, remember the "matching concept" and "accrual accounting" concepts that both say you recognize an expense when it happens—*regardless* of when you pay for it? That is an accounting "rule." Knowingly under reporting expenses (which over states income) is a serious offense in the "Wall Street" world. I expect folks to take their own financial statements just as seriously.

Are we finished? You think so? Let's check. Let's see if we know the answers to The Seven Questions:

1. **Are the financials correct?** Yes.

2. **What are the unfavorable variances?** Volume, Labor, supplies, and outside services all had unfavorable variances. Other expenses had a favorable variance.

3. **Why did they occur?**

   - **Labor** - unfavorable salary cost driven by higher than budgeted volumes. Cost per registration on budget at $8.50.

   - **Supplies** - $1,699 (2%) of unfavorable cost per UOS variance driven by late month order. Expect next month expense to be lower than budget. Cost per registration over 2% for the month, but under budget 2% on a YTD basis. Remaining variance driven by higher than budgeted volume.

   - **Outside services** - over budget by $31,849. This variance is consistent with prior months and relates to an unbudgeted expense for outsourced collection fees. Increased collections more than offset this expense.

   - **Other expenses** - under budget by $5,000. The budget included an inspection. The inspection did not occur this month. We expect it to occur next month.

4. **Have the events causing the variances been corrected?** There is nothing to correct.

5. **If not, why not, and when will they be corrected?** Since there is nothing to correct, this question is not applicable.

6. **What help do you need to correct them?** Also not applicable.

7. **How are you doing this month?** Hopefully, you know the answer to this question! An example response might be: "Volumes are high again compared to budget. Productivity is below budget on a MH per stat basis, but overtime is higher than budget because of Sue Smith going into premature labor and starting her maternity leave early. The inspection budgeted for last month is taking place next week. I don't know of any other expected variances."

See—that wasn't so bad, was it? Ready to tackle something a little more complex? Let's look at the radiology department. We'll go through the exact same process.

RADIOLOGY

The departmental financial statement is shown on **Exhibit 28** *(page 174),* and the MOR is shown on **Exhibit 34**.

1. Set the stage: Close your eyes and think about what you know. Think about your story.

   • This is May, 2011. The eighth month of the hospital's fiscal year (which ends on September 30, 2011).

   • Based on the daily stat reports you saw, volume was pretty close to budget.

   • Based on the productivity reports you reviewed, you think you beat productivity. Paid MH/Stat were under budget, but you did use some contract labor, which was not budgeted. You are uncertain about how your cost per stat will come out.

   • You do not recall having any unusual expenses occur or come to you for approval, even though Administration did approve you having lunch catered by a local restaurant this month to celebrate National Diagnostic Imaging Week.

2. With this information in mind, look first at the department financial statement (**Exhibit 28**). Start at the top of the page and move down it. Volume first. It does show volume as being very close to budget (in total).

3. Salaries are slightly under budget, but contract labor is over budget *(rows 24 and 25 column C).* When you combine the two, the total dollar amount is over budget. Volume was very close to budget, so labor dollars should be too. Remember, the most important thing is to stay within the budgeted cost per UOS. Look at the MOR on **Exhibit 34**. Scroll down to *row 32*—"Total paid labor cost per UOS." Notice the cost per UOS was over budget. What drove this? It could have been too many hours per UOS, or too much paid per hour—or it could be both. Look at the two rows above—*rows 30 and 31.* Employed cost per UOS was

		A	B	C	D	E	F
	EXHIBIT 34						
	Monthly Operating Review						
	Department: Radiology						
	Month: May 2011						
		Actual	Budget	Volume Adjusted Budget	Variance to Budget	Variance to Vol Adj Budget	Impact Against Vol Adj Budget
				Current Month			
1	**I. VOLUME**						
2	IP exams	3,348	3,100	N/A	248	N/A	N/A
3	OP exams	3,949	4,030	N/A	(81)	N/A	N/A
4	Total Units of Service	7,297	7,130	N/A	167	N/A	N/A
5							
6							
7	**II. LABOR MANAGEMENT**						
8	Productivity:						
9	Employed worked Nursing Hours per UOS			-	-	-	N/A
10	Contract Labor Worked Hours per UOS	0.08	-	-	(0.08)	(0.08)	N/A
11	Other Worked Hours per UOS	1.45	1.49	1.49	0.04	0.04	N/A
12	Total Worked Hours per UOS	1.53	1.49	1.49	(0.04)	(0.04)	N/A
13	Non-Prod Hours per UOS	0.03	0.17	0.17	0.14	0.14	N/A
14	Total Paid Hours per UOS	1.55	1.66	1.66	0.10	0.10	N/A
15	FTEs:						
16	Employed worked Nursing FTEs	0.00	0.00	0.00	0.00	0.00	N/A
17	Contract Labor FTEs	3.45	0.00	0.00	(3.45)	(3.45)	N/A
18	Other worked FTEs	59.69	60.14	61.55	0.44	1.86	N/A
19	Total worked FTEs	63.14	60.14	61.55	(3.00)	(1.59)	N/A
20	Non-Prod FTEs	1.05	6.68	6.84	5.64	5.79	N/A
21	Total Paid FTEs	64.19	66.82	68.39	2.63	4.20	N/A
22	Rate:						
23	Average Hourly Rate - Payroll	$17.50	$17.42	$17.42	$(0.08)	$(0.08)	N/A
24	Average Hourly Rate - Contract	$26.25	$-	$-	$(26.25)	$(26.25)	N/A
25	Total AHR	$18.91	$17.42	$17.42	$(1.49)	$(1.49)	N/A
26							N/A
27	Premium Hours (OT+CL+CB)	858	236	242	(622)	(616)	N/A
28	Premium Hours as Percentage of Worked Hours	7.69%	2.00%	2.00%	-5.69%	-5.69%	N/A
29	**III. EXPENSES**						
30	Employed Cost per UOS	$27.19	$28.84	$28.84	$1.65	$1.65	$12,024
31	Contract Labor Cost per UOS	$2.19	$-	$-	$(2.19)	$(2.19)	$(15,987)
32	Total Paid Labor Cost per UOS	$29.38	$28.84	$28.84	$(0.54)	$(0.54)	$(3,963)
33	Supply costs per UOS	$2.84	$2.78	$2.78	$(0.06)	$(0.06)	$(406)
34	Other Expenses per UOS	$0.27	$2.34	$2.34	$2.07	$2.07	$15,092
35	Total Cost per UOS	$32.49	$33.96	$33.96	$1.47	$1.47	$10,723

actually under budget. But it was only under budget by $1.65, which was not enough to offset the contract labor cost per UOS overage of $2.19. The net is the $.54 over per UOS. Also, look at *column F on row 32*. The $.54 overage translated to being over budget by $3,963. so how do the amounts in *column F on rows 30 and 31* relate to the variance columns on **Exhibit 28** *(page 174, rows 24 and 25, column C)*? Notice the contract labor variance is the same. but the salary variance on **Exhibit 28** *row 24* is a favorable variance of $7,196, while the variance in *column F* of **Exhibit 34**, *page 199, row 30* is $12,024. Why are the numbers different? Remember, *column F* is the variance on a "volume adjusted" budget. Since volume was higher than budget, *column F* computes how much you would be expected to spend given the extra volume. It "re-computes" a budget based on the budgeted cost per UOS times the actual volume experienced. Actual volume was 7,297 UOS. Budgeted cost per UOS is $28.84. 7,297 x $28.84 = $210,457. So $210,457 is the re-computed, volume-adjusted budget for hospital salaries. You spent $198,433. The difference between what you spent, and the re-computed, volume-adjusted budget is $12,024. Voila! That is the amount shown on *column F, row 30*. Now that we've solved that question, let's get back to explaining your variance. Zoom to **Exhibit 34**, *row 14*—Paid MH/Stat. As you expected from reviewing productivity throughout the month, you are under budget there. Wow! The favorable variance of .10 *(column D)* is 6% under budget. So if paid hours per stat were 6% under budget, then the only way the cost per UOS could be over budget is that the AHR is over budget. And it is. Look at *rows 23, 24, and 25. Row 24* shows that the AHR paid to hospital employees was very close to budget: $17.50 on a budget of $17.42 (within 1%). But the overall AHR *(shown on row 25)* is $18.91 on a budget of $17.42 (a 9% variance—Ouch!) because of the use of contract labor. So there it is. The unfavorable labor variance is because of contract labor. From a productivity perspective, you actually did well at 6% under budget on a paid MH/Stat. But is it because you truly managed well, or was some of it a fluke? Let's look. The Productivity and FTE sections of the MOR on **Exhibit 34** *(page 199)* show some more details that will help answer our question. We already talked about MH/UOS being under budget *(row 14)*. But look above *row 14 to rows 12 and 13*. A different story emerges! *Row 12* shows that worked hours per UOS were actually over budget. But non-productive time was significantly under budget. It was under budget enough to compensate for the worked hours per UOS being over budget. Chances are, you did not orchestrate the non-productive time being under budget. It's possible, but most managers are focused on productive hours being enough to get the work done. Non-productive time falls where it may. So although the ultimate goal is to keep the cost per UOS at or under budget (which means I am OK if you get there because non-productive time was under budget, even though productive time was over budget), the true indicator of a good manager is worked hours per UOS being under or at budget. If you think that doesn't seem quite fair, think of the reverse situation. How would you feel if you worked hard, and ended the month with worked hours per UOS being under budget. But because of some mandated company training (counted as non-productive), your non-productive time was over budget, pushing your total paid hours per UOS over budget. Would you feel as though you should have been held accountable to reduce worked hours below productivity standards to do the work in order to compensate for the training hours? In my view, no, you should not. If productivity is over budget, I only hold managers accountable for the *worked* hours. To me, an unfavorable variance for worked hours per UOS needs to be explained, even if paid hours per UOS is under due to non-productive time being under budget. If this was your department, and we were meeting to discuss your department performance, I would have two concerns regarding labor. The overage of worked hours per UOS, and the cost per UOS being over. Since we know that the cost per UOS variance is caused by the use of contract labor, I would want to know why it was used, and if it was still being used. You should know the answers to both of these questions. What are some possible answers? Look at **Exhibit 34** (*page 199*), *row 17, column A*. You used 3.45 FTEs of contract labor. The budget was zero. So what happened that you needed 3.45 FTEs that you did not have? Someone quit or was terminated? Someone went out on FMLA? The increased volume may be part of the reason. Look at *row 19, columns B and C. Column B* is the 60.14 budgeted FTEs, but *column C* shows that because of volume, you actually needed 61.55 FTEs. That's an extra 1.41 FTEs. Let's say that is part of your explanation. Let's say the other two FTEs of contract labor were needed because you have 2 vacancies in the department. Maybe that is why your non-productive time is so low (you have not been letting people take time off because you are short staffed). So have the positions been filled, and is the contract labor gone? Let's say that one of the positions have been hired. One new person has started, but is being trained. The other position is waiting for the job requisition to be approved. Because of the required training, you do not anticipate being able to eliminate the contract labor until next month at the earliest. My next question to you would be "OK, then, what other changes are you making in the department to cover this added expense?" We'll come back to this question later. We still have not talked about the worked hours per UOS being over budget. Look at *row 12* on **Exhibit 34** (*page 199*). it shows that worked hours per UOS were over budget by .04. This is only 2.6% of the budgeted 1.49. Applying my 5% rule, this variance would be considered immaterial, and no explanation would be required (especially since the non-productive time more than offset it).

As we've previously pointed out, volume fluctuates throughout the day so that exactly hitting a productivity metric is impossible. If any of this labor discussion confused you, you may want to re-read **Chapter 13** on labor management, or **Chapter 17** on understanding an MOR.

4. Looking at the department financial statement (**Exhibit 28**, *page 174*), supply cost was over budget by $871. However, we know volume was higher than budget. Look at **Exhibit 34** *(page 199), row 33.* Supply cost per UOS was, in fact, over budget. But only by 2%. That unfavorable 2% variance resulting in a $406 unfavorable supply variance *(row 33, column F).* The remainder of the unfavorable variance (the difference between the $871 and the $406) is simply extra expense required to accommodate the increased volume. Because the variance is so small, no explanation is needed.

5. Maintenance and Repairs is under budget by $10,500 for the month (**Exhibit 28** [*page 174], row 28*). This would appear very suspicious to me. Looking at the YTD expense of $82,356, it shows the monthly average was running around $10,000 per month. So maybe we changed something such that the entire $12,000 budget is not needed, but I would wonder if something was missing here. As the department manager, you would probably know. This line item includes both maintenance and repairs. Maintenance refers usually to annual maintenance contracts. The fees for these contracts (especially for imaging equipment) can be quite large, and may be set up to show 1/12th of the annual payment each month. So maybe you have some equipment that has a monthly charge of $10,000. it appears to be missing. If so, you need to contact finance and let them know. Perhaps the remaining budget of $500 was for repairs, and you didn't have any this month.

6. Outside services is under budget by $3,200 (**Exhibit 28**, *page 174, row 29*). Is this correct? Let's say you took over the department a year ago, and were shocked to find out that none of the policies and procedures had been updated in five years. Therefore, you budgeted to have a consultant come in and update them for you. For the first seven months of the year, you have been spending $3,000 per month for this service. But starting this month, you feel the task has reached a manageable size. You and your staff are now completing the task yourselves. So yes, zero expense this month for outside services is correct. And it is also your answer to the question posed above regarding what changes you made in the department to compensate for the use of contract labor! If you go back to **Exhibit 34** *(page 199), row 32, column F,* you see the excess labor cost per UOS cost $3,963. You covered $3,200 of it by not using the consultant this month. Great!

7. Other expenses are under budget by $1,000 for the month (**Exhibit 28** (*page 174*), *row 35*). This looks very suspicious to me. Looking at the YTD columns, I also see that the YTD variance is under budget by $1,000. This strongly suggests that there should be a $1,500 expense charged here every month (there has been exactly that amount every month until now). I would suspect that this is a missed accrual. As manager, you should know what the $1,500 budget was for. If you do not, go back to your budget and look. If this is a missing accrual, let finance know. For discussion purposes, let's say it was an accrual for accreditation fees that was missed.

8. Don't forget the last question to ask yourself during your review! Remember, before you started you closed your eyes and imagined your story and what you expected to see. Did you see everything? Is there anything missing? Yes, there is. The lunch you had catered is not here. Perhaps you put it on your credit card and have not yet turned in your expense report. But it should be accrued. Even though this expense is not budgeted, and therefore will create an unfavorable variance, it is still important for you to get it accrued this month, when the expense occurred. Administration approved spending the money, knowing it was unbudgeted, so you have nothing to apologize for.

OK, you think you are done? Let's see if we know the answers to The Seven Questions:

1. **Are the financials correct?** No. Three accruals were missing. The $10,000 monthly fee for a maintenance contract, and a $1,000 accrual for accreditation fees were both missed. In addition, an accrual is needed to recognize the expense for the luncheon. Finance has been notified.

2. **What are the unfavorable variances?** Contract Labor and supplies both had unfavorable variances. Volume and all other expenses had favorable variances.

3. **Why did they occur?**

   - **Labor**—The combined total of salaries and contract labor were over budget by $8,791 (**Exhibit 28** [*page 174*], *rows 24 + 25, column C*). Paid Labor Cost per UOS was over budget by $.54 causing an unfavorable variance of $3,463. The remaining unfavorable variance was caused by volume being over budget. Although worked hours per UOS were slightly over budget, non-productive hours were under budget, so that in total, paid hours per UOS were under budget. The unfavorable labor cost per UOS variance was caused by the unbudgeted use of 3.45 FTEs of contract labor. 1.41 FTEs were needed to cover volume being over budget. Two FTEs were necessary to cover vacancies in the department. Most of the $3,463 unfavorable variance was offset by eliminating the consulting fees for updating policies and procedures. $3,200 was budgeted for this for the month. We have taken the project in house to complete ourselves, and eliminated this expense.

- **Supplies**—Supply expense was over budget by $871. $406 was caused by supply cost per UOS being over budget—immaterial. The remaining variance was caused by volume being over budget.

4. **Have the events causing the variances been corrected?** Not yet. 1.5 FTEs of contract labor are still here.

5. **If not, why not, and when will they be corrected?** One of the FTEs should be gone next month. We have filled one of the vacancies, and the new person has started and should complete training by the end of the month. The other position is still vacant.

6. **What help do you need to correct them?** We need the job requisition to replace the second vacancy to be approved.

7. **How are you doing this month?** Good. Volume is down slightly, so we have reduced the use of contract labor, even though we still have a vacancy. We continue to progress with updating the policies and procedures, and expect to be able to finish it ourselves by the end of the fiscal year, as planned.

That wasn't too bad, was it? Hopefully by now, things are starting to click and fall into place. You see the story when you look at the financials, or know that there is an error if the story isn't there. Last, but not least, let's look at a Nursing unit.

NURSING UNIT

We will use the department financial statement we used in the previous chapter, shown on **Exhibit 29** (*page 176*), and the related MOR, shown on **Exhibit 32** (*page 180*). We looked at these documents before, but it was only to understand the information contained in them, and how to read them. Here we will look at the variances, and understand what story they tell about what happened in the department last month.

1. Set the stage: Close your eyes and think about what you know. Think about your story.

- This is May, 2011. The eighth month of the hospital's fiscal year (which ends on September 30, 2011).

- Based on the daily stat reports you saw, volume was under budget by almost 10%. Census was 48 for the month, on a budget of 52.

- Your hospital does not have daily productivity reports. You have not seen a productivity report. You lost a large number of clerical staff to a newly opened competitor in town, and had to use more nurses to compensate, but in total you feel you stayed tightly within the staffing matrix used to run the department (and to prepare the budget). The extra use of nurses did require contract labor, even with the lower than budgeted census.

- You rented some wound vacs during the month, but this is normal, and you do not think utilization was in excess of what was budgeted based on your review of the budget at the beginning of the month. You also had an employee attend a seminar this month. The cost was $200 for registration, plus her expenses. You just signed her expense report for those expenses. It was $300.

2. With this information in mind, look first at the department financial statement (**Exhibit 29**, *page 176*). Start at the top of the page and move down it. Volume first. It does show volume as being exactly what you saw on the daily reports. The reason I have made a point to look at this on each review is that it is very important that the department statistic be correct. If it is wrong, then the productivity, labor cost per unit of service and supply cost per unit of service will all be wrong. You should always look at your department statistic. Learn how to validate it if you do not know. Many hospitals capture statistics when revenue charges are captured. If revenue is captured by someone keying in charges manually, errors are very possible. It is also possible that if the month ended on a weekend, the charges for the last day (or last two days) did not get entered. You should always know and understand how your department statistic is generated, and how to validate it.

3. Looking down **Exhibit 29**, *page 176, rows 24 and 25*, you see that the combined labor expense is over budget by $15,784 ($4,676 - $20,460), even though volume was less than budget. Ouch! Looks like you've got some explaining to do! Remember in the last chapter we referred to the MOR as the translation dictionary? Looks like we need some help translating, so let's go look at it. **Exhibit 32** *(page 180)* contains a plethora of information to help us sort this out. First, how bad is it? Remember, the ultimate goal is to keep the labor cost per UOS at or under budget. Did we do that? No. Look at *row 32*. The total actual labor cost per UOS came in at $333.43 against a budget of $297.99. The impact of that variance was $57,661. Ouch! But wait, you say? You agree with the $20,460 contact labor variance *(row 31 column F)*, but the salary variance shown on *row 30 column F* is $37,201, even though the salary variance shown on **Exhibit 29** *(page 176)* is only $4,676. Why aren't these numbers the same? As we talked about previously, it is because *column F* is adjusted to accommodate the difference between actual and budgeted volume. Since volume was less than budget, you were expected to spend less than budget. But you didn't. The difference

between the volume-adjusted salary budget and your actual salary spend is the $37,201. So in total, when you combine the salary variance and the contract labor variance, the impact was $57,661 *(row 32, column F)*. "Oh dear" you think. "I am in big trouble! This is even worse than I thought!" But you thought you had managed your department as best you could given the situation. Let's dig deeper. Look down the Labor management section of the MOR *(rows 7 through 28)*. There are several things to notice:

a. *Row 12* shows total worked hours per UOS as being 9.25 on a budget of 8.60. But remember from **Chapter 13** that when volume is less than budget in a Nursing unit, productivity will be worse usually? Go back to your staffing matrix and compare the worked hours per UOS for a census of 48 to a census of 52. Using our matrix (shown in **Exhibit 10** *(page 77)*, the worked hours per UOS for a census of 48 was 9.42. You came in at 9.25. You beat the staffing matrix. The budget variance is caused by the lower census. Phew! One (big) variance explained!

b. OK, you've explained the variance in total worked hours. But we aren't done yet. Look at *rows 9 through 11, columns A, B and C*. See how actual nursing hours per UOS are substantially over budget *(row 9)*, while non-nursing hours per UOS are only half of what was budgeted? If you look at *row 18*, you can see how this translated into FTEs. Quite a difference! This is an illustration of a skill mix variance. Here is a great example of where the numbers tell the story. Here is where your use of nurses to compensate for clerical staff vacancies shows up. What difference did it make? Look at *row 23*: the AHR is higher. You used more hours of higher-paid labor, and fewer hours of lower-paid labor. The effect was to increase your overall AHR. Remember we said in the previous chapter that $.50 per hour could cost a 500 bed hospital $5 million per year? That's why it matters.

4. Supply expense is under budget per **Exhibit 29** *(page 176, row 27)*, and within $.03 cost per UOS per **Exhibit 32**, *page 180, row 33*. The $.03 variance only has an impact of $45 *(row 33, column F)*. No explanation needed.

5. All other expenses are under budget.

6. Last step. Remember? Close your eyes and think back to your story. Is there anything you expected to see, but did not? Yes. Remember the seminar that you just signed the expense check to reimburse $300? It is not here. You need to let finance know.

Think you're done? Let's see. The Seven Questions:

1. **Are the financials correct?** No. An expense check for an employee for $300 needs to be accrued. Finance has been notified.

2. **What are the unfavorable variances?** Volume was under budget. Salaries and contract labor were both over budget.

3. **Why did they occur?** Worked hours per UOS were over budget, but actually under budget when the staffing matrix is applied to the lower volume. A new competitor hospital offered a higher wage than we pay for clerical support staff. We lost 15 FTEs. Due to the large number of vacancies, we backfilled with nurses. The excess need for nurses generated a need for contract labor. The higher rate for nurses and contract labor caused a higher than budgeted AHR.

4. **Have the events causing the variances been corrected?** Not yet. Nurses are still being utilized to backfill for the clerical support vacancies. Contract labor has been eliminated.

5. **If not, why not, and when will they be corrected?** Human Resources is looking in to increasing our hourly rate to compete with the new hospital. We have posted the positions, but are having trouble attracting applicants, as the new hospital is still hiring.

6. **What help do you need to correct them?** Have human resources expedite adjusting the hourly wage.

7. **How are you doing this month?** Things, unfortunately, are about the same.

This last department was an example of a not-so-fun review. But—you knew your story. And it wasn't that you did not manage your department. Management understands that things happen. You must respond, and you are responsible for keeping your department functioning. They just expect you to do it in an informed fashion, which means knowing how your decisions affect the hospital financially. And being able to articulate those decisions and choices at the end of the month.

The key is to be engaged in your department. Know what is going on. Be ready and able to articulate your story. And if things have happened that knocked you off track, have a plan to fix it. As a great boss and mentor taught me, "Hope is *not* a strategy."

Chapter 18 Self Review Questions

1. Name The Seven Questions.

2. What are the three steps to use to prepare for an MOR?

3. What are the two questions to ask yourself in determining if the expenses on the financial statements are correct?

4. On **Exhibit 34** *(page 199)* for radiology, *row 19 Column C* shows a volume Adjusted budget of 61.55 Worked FTEs. Why is this number higher than the budgeted FTE number shown in column B?

5. Using **Exhibit 34** *(page 199)* for Radiology, how did the department achieve a better than budget Paid MH/Stat?

Self Review
Questions and Answers

CHAPTER 1 SELF REVIEW QUESTIONS

1. If your hospital's midnight census over the past week was 528, 578, 543, 509, 551, 537, and 549, what was the ADC for the week?

   Answer: (528+578+543+509+551+537+549)/7 = 542

2. If your hospital had inpatient revenues of $1,597,231 and outpatient revenues of $782,344, what is your adjustment factor?

   Answer: ($1,597,231+$782,344)/$1,597,231 = 1.49

3. If your hospital had inpatient days totaling 10,168 during the month, and an adjustment factor of 1.83, how many APDs did you have?

   Answer: 10,168 x 1.83 = 18,607.

4. If total worked hours during the most recent 14 day pay period in your department were 4,480, how many worked FTEs were there?

   Answer: 1 FTE = 80 hours, so 4,480/80 = 56.

5. Your Lab department's productivity is .15 MH/Stat. The lab in a competing hospital has a productivity stat of .20 MH/Stat. Who is more productive?

   Answer: With productivity, less is better. Since your MH/Stat is less than your competitor's, you are more productive.

CHAPTER 2 SELF REVIEW QUESTIONS

1. If the DRG payment for a diagnosis with a weight of 1.25 is $12,500, how much would the DRG payment be at the same hospital for a diagnosis with a CMI of 1.56?

   Answer: If $12,500 is the payment for a DRG with a weight of 1.25, then the payment for a DRG with a weight of 1.0 must be $12,500/1.25 = $10,000. If the payment for a DRG with a weight of 1.0 is $10,000, then the payment for a DRG with a weight of 1.56 must be $10,000 x 1.56 = $15,600.

2. If your hospital's variable cost per inpatient day is $1,800, and the DRG payment for a particular patient is $6,000, what is the hospital's margin if the patient stays 3 days? 5 days?

Answer: For the 3 day stay, the reimbursement is $6,000, less the cost of (3 x $1,800) = $6,000 - $5,400 = $600. For the 5 day stay, the reimbursement is still $6,000, less the cost of (5 x $1,800) = $6,000 - $9,000 = ($3,000).

3. Two accounts were written off. One was written off to charity, and the other was written off to bad debt. Which account had collection efforts?

Answer: while the obvious answer is the account written off to bad debt, it is possible that both accounts had collection efforts, since sometimes collections efforts have begun already before a patient completes paperwork required to qualify for charity.

4. What is the difference between a denial and bad debt?

Answer: A denial comes from an insurance carrier who claims that services were not needed or not authorized, and therefore they are not responsible for paying the bill. Bad debt comes from a patient who chooses not to pay a bill that s/he is responsible for. Their reason may also be because they feel they were given care or services that were unnecessary, but "denials" only come from insurance companies.

5. If your hospital's Gross Revenues were $29,773,615, Net Revenue was $12,359,123, and Contractual Allowances were $15,897,584, how much was written off to charity?

Answer: Net Revenue = Gross Revenues - Contractual Allowances- Charity. So if Gross Revenues ($29,773,615) - Contractual Allowances ($15,897,584) = $13,876,031, and Net Revenue is only $12,359,123, the missing piece is Charity. So Charity must be the difference: $13,876,031 - $12,359,123 = $1,516,908.

CHAPTER 3 SELF REVIEW QUESTIONS

1. Does the Accounts Receivable Ledger feed into the General Ledger, or does the General Ledger feed into the Accounts Receivable Ledger?

Answer: The General Ledger is the "mother" ledger—everything feeds into it. Therefore, the Accounts Receivable Ledger feeds into the General Ledger.

2. If you needed to know what account number to use to charge a plane ticket to on your expense report, what document would you likely look at—the G/L, the TB, or the Chart of Accounts?

Answer: You would likely look at the Chart of Accounts, although if you were familiar with the account and knew generally what it was called, if you perused the TB, you could probably find it.

3. If your departmental operating statement showed an expense that you didn't recognize, and you wanted to investigate it, what report would you ask for from accounting?

Answer: You would want to ask for the G/L Detail. This is the only report that will show all the activity posted to an account.

4. If you were helping the CFO with a project, and were asked to find out what total Accounts Receivable were at June 30, 2008, what report would you want to review to find the answer to that question?

Answer: You would want to look at the company's Balance Sheet as of June 30, 2008.

5. Your departmental operating statement is a subset of what financial report for your hospital?

Answer: Since your operating statement shows numbers that reflect activity over a period of time, it is a subset of the hospital's Income Statement.

CHAPTER 4 SELF STUDY QUESTIONS

1. What is the difference between a Business Plan and a Strategic Plan?

Answer: Some people use the terms interchangeably, but a Business Plan usually refers to the first Strategic Plan ever prepared. It is put together for potential investors when starting a business. Once a business is up and running, a Strategic Plan should be in place at all times.

2. What is the connection between a Strategic Plan and a Budget?

Answer: A Budget is the "finance-ese" presentation of a one-year slice of the Strategic Plan.

3. True or False: A Strategic Plan doesn't need to be updated every year.

Answer: False. A well run business will update it's Strategic Plan each year.

4. Which of the following questions would you expect to hear a CFO discussing at the annual budget planning meeting?

a. How many patients do we expect to care for next year compared to this year?

b. Are there any plans to add or discontinue services?

c. Are there any plans to make changes to the employee benefit plans?

d. All of the above.

Answer: d. All of the above

5. Using the example in Exhibit 2, what was the expected impact of inflation on next year's Income from Operations?

Answer: $3,537 (see row 17, column D)

CHAPTER 5 SELF REVIEW QUESTIONS

1. If a dollar spent is not Operating or Capital, what is it?

Answer: it is impossible to not be either Operating OR Capital: every dollar spent must be one or the other.

2. Is depreciation expense an Operating expense or a Capital expense?

Answer: Depreciation is an Operating expense used to spread the cost of a Capital item over multiple years.

3. Which of the following is not a requirement for an item to be considered Capital?

a. It must be a tangible asset

b. It must have a useful life greater than 1 year

c. It must cost a large sum of money

d. All of the above are requirements for an item to be considered capital.
   Answer: d. All of the above

4. If a gym membership lasts 3 years, and costs a lot of money, is it capital?
   Answer: No. A capital asset must be a TANGIBLE asset you can touch.

5. Is a family vacation a capital or an operating expense?
   Answer: it is an operating expense. Regardless of how much it costs, it is not a tangible asset, nor does it have a useful life greater than one (1) year.

CHAPTER 6 SELF REVIEW QUESTIONS

1. You are the Director for the Pharmacy Department. Budget preparation is beginning for FY2012. Your hospital requires strategic initiative requests be prepared for both operating and capital requests.

• You would like the hospital to add automated drug dispensing equipment to the ED.

• Research shows this equipment will improve dispensing and charge capture.

• It will also reduce staffing costs by 1 FTE. This FTE earns $75,000 a year, plus benefits which run approximately 20% of salary costs.

• The equipment can be purchased for $100,000. In addition, IT will need to write an interface. IT has given you an estimate of $5,000 to build and test the interface.

Complete a Strategic Initiative Request Form for the request.

   Answer: Compare what you have prepared to the example opposite.

CHAPTER 7 SELF REVIEW QUESTIONS

1. What is the goal when setting a statistic for a department?
   Answer: to choose a measurement that is most closely relevant to the resources used to do the tasks carried out by that department.

2. Why is budgeting statistics the single most important element of the budget process?
   Answer: Because volume drives 100% of patient revenue and well over 50% of operating expenses.

3. What is the general formula for budgeting volume?
   Answer: Prior year volume less discontinued or closed services plus new services plus expected growth = budgeted volume for next year.

4. If ADC for the year is budgeted to be 300, and ALOS is budgeted at 3.3 days, how many discharges are being budgeted?

J Lee Community Hospital **Budget Request**	Budget Dept Use Only	Request # _____
	Approved?	Y N

Fiscal Year Ending		2012
Department Name		Pharmacy
Name of Request		Drug Dispensing Equipment
Total Money Requested:		
Operating Funds		($90,000)
Capital Funds (quote must be attached)		$105,000
Capital Requests only:		
Fiscal quarter funds are needed (circle one)		(1) 2 3 4
Priority rating (A = Mandatory, B = Urgent, C = Needed but not urgent)		A (B) C
Is this request associated with compliance with a new regulatory requirement?		Y (N)
Is this request associated with compliance with an existing but deficient regulatory requirement?		Y (N)
If you answered Yes to either question, please reference the code at issue.		
Describe your request:		
Add automated drug dispensing equipment to the Emergency Department		
Describe the benefits to the hospital of granting your request		
Drug dispensing will be more accurate and charge capture will improve		
Describe the risks to the hospital if your request is not granted		
Manual drug dispensing increases the risk of medication errors		
Will granting your request increase Net Revenues?		Y (N)
If so, how much per month (detail needs to be attached)?		
If so, what month will revenues begin?		J F M A M J J A S O N D
Will granting your request increase expenses?		Y (N)
If so, how much per month (detail needs to be attached)?		Reduction of $90,000
If so, what month will expenses begin?		J F M A M J J A S O N D
Will granting your request require additional FTEs to be hired?		Y (N)
If so, how many?		Reduction of 1 FTE
If so, what month will the increase begin?		J F M A M J J A S O N D
Does this request have IT implications (hardware/software/interfaces/training)?		Y (N)
Prepared by (printed name)	Edward Dunn	
Submitted by (Director Signature)	*Edward Dunn*	
Date submitted	10/26/2011	

Answer: 300 ADC x 365 days = 109,500 inpatient days. 109,500 inpatient days / 3.3 ALOS = 33,182 discharges.

5. If Lab volumes this year averaged 10 tests per adjusted discharge, and next year's budget calls for 10,000 discharges, an adjustment factor of 1.75, and a reduction in utilization of 5%, how many lab tests should be budgeted for next year?

Answer: 10,000 discharges x 1.75 = 17,500 adjusted discharges. 17,500 adjusted discharges x 10 tests per adjusted discharges = 175,000 tests. 175,000 tests—5% reduction = 166,250 tests to be budgeted.

CHAPTER 8 SELF REVIEW QUESTIONS

1. Name the three approaches to budgeting labor.

Answer: 100% Variable, 100% fixed, and combination of semi-variable and semi-fixed.

2. Compute the annual budget for salaries for the Department of Surgery using the following information:

10,000 surgeries at an average of 65 minutes per surgery

Target productivity for worked hours is .10 hours per minute

Non-productive add-on is 10%. AHR is $30.

Answer: 10,000 surgeries x 65 minutes per surgery = 650,000 minutes. 650,000 minutes x .10 hours per minute = 65,000 worked hours. 65,000 worked hours + 10% non-productive time = 71,500 hours. 71,500 hours x $30/hr = $2,145,000 budgeted salary cost per year.

3. Using the information from question #2 above, how many worked FTEs need to be budgeted?

Answer: 65,000 worked hours / 2,080 hours per FTE = 31.25 FTEs.

4. Using the statistic (minutes) information from #2 above, what is the total cost per UOS (including non-productive time)?

Answer: $2,145,000/650,000 = $3.30 cost per minute of surgery.

5. If HIM has 10 FTEs and the AHR of the department is $15, and non-productive time is 10%, how much money should be budgeted for the month of February (a 28 day month)?

Answer: 1 FTE works 2,080 hours per year / 365 days = 5.6986 hours per day. So in February, one FTE works 5.6986 hours per day x 28 days = 160 hours. 10 FTEs work 160 x 10 = 1,600 hours at $15 = $24,000.

CHAPTER 9 SELF REVIEW QUESTIONS

1. Which type of classification are each of the following:

Office supplies

(A natural classification)

Blood

(Could be either a department or a natural classification)

Antibiotics

(A natural classification)

Pharmacy

(A department)

Lab

(A department)

2. Name the 2 types of volume initiatives that can impact your supply volume budget.

Answer: Natural class specific and Department specific.

3. Name the 2 types of price initiatives that may affect your supply cost budget.

Answer: Natural class specific and department specific.

4. If pharmacy supplies were $25,000,000, and supply chain initiatives were being developed to reduce utilization by 5%, and inflation was expected to run 8%, what other information would you need to know to calculate the supply budget for pharmacy?

Answer: you would need to know what the prior year volume was and what the budgeted volume for next year is. Without this information, you cannot calculate the impact of reduced utilization or changes in hospital volume on supply spend.

5. If current year Lab supply spending was $250,000 on 2,500,000 tests, performed on 100,000 patients, compute next year's supply budget using the following assumptions:

volume is budgeted at 110,000 patients

inflation is 2%

Supply chain initiatives are being designed to reduce utilization by 10% per patient.

Answer: Current year utilization is 2,500,000 tests divided by 100,000 patients = 25 tests per patient at a cost of $250,000/2,500,000 = $.10 per test. If utilization is to decline by 10%, then tests per patient will decline from 25 tests per patient to 22.5 tests per patient. With volume budgeted at 110,000 patients, the number of tests performed will be 110,000 x 22.5 = 2,475,000. The cost per test, after inflation, will be $.10 + 2% = $.102. So 2,475,000 tests at $.102 per test = $252,450.

CHAPTER 10 SELF REVIEW QUESTIONS

---

1. Name 3 common fixed expenses.

Answer: There are many. Three examples are: maintenance, repairs, rentals.

2. If your hospital outsources a patient service, such as interpreting, should that expense be budgeted as a fixed or a variable expense?

Answer: Unless you have a highly sophisticated budget system, these types of services will likely be budgeted as a fixed expense. It will important for you, as the person responsible for the budget, to consider if there are reasons why the budget should be increased due to budgeted increases in hospital volume. Likewise, perhaps a new arrangement is being made to bring the service in house. Then the fixed expenses budget may be reduced or eliminated, while staffing may need to be increased (this is an example of a strategic initiative—see Chapter 6 for details on how to approach budgeting such a change)

3. Even though repairs can vary greatly from month to month, and from hospital to hospital, they are considered to be a fixed expense. Why?

   Answer: Fixed expenses are expenses that although they may vary, they do not vary because of changes in patient volume.

4. If you have a once-a-year expense that typically occurs in the last month of the year, which approach will be best for preparing the forecast for the remainder of the year to ensure that item is captured?

   Answer: Using the budget for the remaining months. If the YTD actual expenses are pro-rated, the expense will be missed since it has not occurred yet.

5. If your department spending on forms has totaled $100,000 through 10 months of the year, and the remaining budget is $10,000, will applying the prorated approach to forecast the remainder of the year yield an accurate baseline for next year's budget?

   Answer: Probably not. It appears the YTD monthly average has been $10,000 per month, but the remaining budget is only $5,000 per month. More information is needed to know for sure. Perhaps a new regulatory requirement was issued, requiring a 1-time forms expense of $50,000. Excluding that 1-time expense, the monthly average has been $5,000—making the remaining budget adequate.

CHAPTER 11 SELF REVIEW QUESTIONS

---

1. Name the six key pieces of information you need to get a copy of when the budget has been completed.

   Answer: your volume statistic, your department Profit and Loss statement, your labor management budgets and metrics, your supply budgets and metrics, supporting detail for fixed expenses, and your approved capital budget.

2. You are a revenue-generating department. Why does your department Profit and Loss statement usually look as though you make a lot of money?

   Answer: Because revenue deductions have not been taken away.

3. If you don't understand some things in your budget when you receive it, what should you do?

   Answer: make an appointment with finance to go over it to help you understand it (or possibly identify an error!).

4. What is the simplest way to get a quick handle on what changes there are in your budget?

   Answer: Compare the next year's budget with current year actual volumes and metrics to see what is budgeted to change.

5. Why is it important to review your approved capital budget together with your operating budget?

Answer: To make sure they fit together. If you anticipated approval for some capital equipment that was to affect expenses, and the capital did not get approved, you need to make sure the operating expenses reflect this.

CHAPTER 12 SELF REVIEW QUESTIONS

1. What is the single most important statistic to know and carry around in your head?

Answer: Volume.

2. When would a seasoned manager look at the February budget to see what the February budgeted volume is to be?

Answer: Mid-january.

3. Why are hospital discharges a better volume indicator than census?

Answer: Because most payors pay based on discharges. Two patients staying three days each generate twice the revenue that one patient staying six days generates.

4. Why is it important to look at hospital volume in addition to department volume?

Answer: Department volume may not necessarily indicate hospital volume in many departments. For example, high lab volume may simply be some physicians ordering high volumes of tests on a few very sick patients.

5. If discharges month-to-date through the 18th of a 30 day month are 600, and the budget for the month is 980, is the hospital trending to end the month ahead of budget, behind budget, or right on budget?

Answer: Ahead of budget. 600 discharges in 18 days is an average of 33.33 discharges per day. 33.33 discharges per day x 30 days = 1,000 projected discharges. If the budget is 980, then 1,000 discharges will exceed budget.

CHAPTER 13 SELF REVIEW QUESTIONS

1. If you are a department managed as a "Fixed" department, what does that mean for labor management purposes?

Answer: it means you are budgeted a "fixed" number of FTEs that you are expected to use to run your department.

2. What are the numerator and denominator used for labor productivity?

Answer: the numerator is Man Hours. The denominator is the department statistic.

3. Name the six possible reasons a fixed department's productivity may be off from budget.

Answer:

a) The budget is wrong.

b) The budget is correct, but different than requested.

c) The staffing model has changed since the budget was prepared.

d) Non-productive time is over budget.

e) Extenuating circumstances.

f) The manager blew it.

4. If volume is higher than budget in a department with fixed staffing, will productivity be over or under budget?

Answer: It will likely be under budget. If no staff are added, then the numerator (Man Hours) stays the same, while the denominator (volume) increases—thereby giving a smaller ratio.

5. If your labor management report shows that your MH/stat is over budget, while your cost per UOS is under budget, will your CFO be upset?

Answer: Probably not. Cost per UOS is the ultimate goal.

CHAPTER 14 SELF REVIEW QUESTIONS

---

1. Why should you monitor expenses other than labor during the month?

Answer: You need to know what to expect when you receive your financials at the end of the month. Otherwise you will never know if they are correct.

2. Name one way to keep track of other expenses.

Answer: Keep a log or folder with copies of invoices for large or unusual items.

3. Why is it important to keep the CFO informed of large or unusual expenses that are being incurred?

Answer: You have no idea what information the CFO may be passing along to other members of management, the hospital Board, or investors. If you know of a large or unusual (especially unbudgeted) expense, you should always notify the CFO.

Chapter 15 has no Self Review Questions

CHAPTER 16 SELF REVIEW QUESTIONS

---

1. Name the two types of accounting.

Answer: Cash basis and Accrual basis.

2. With no intervention, which type of accounting will your financial statements reflect?

Answer: Cash basis.

3. If an expense is incurred in April, the invoice is entered into Accounts Payable in May, and paid in June, with no intervention, what month will the expense show up on the financial statements?

Answer: Probably May when it is entered into Accounts Payable.

4. If a $100 expense is incurred in April, the invoice is entered into Accounts Payable in June, and paid in July, if the expense is accrued in April, but not re-accrued in May, what will the May expense reflect?

Answer: $(100). The accrual from April would have reversed generating a negative expense. Since the invoice had still not been recorded, there would be nothing to offset the negative amount.

5. Using the example from #4 above, what activity should the General ledger show for the month of June if everything was done correctly?

Answer: An accrual should have been made in both April and May. The May accrual would have reversed in June, generating a $(100). This negative expense would have been offset by a charge of $100 when the invoice was entered into Accounts Payable. Therefore, although 2 entries were recorded, the net expense for the month would be $0.

CHAPTER 17 SELF REVIEW QUESTIONS

---

1. Name the two most common reports you will use to perform month end review.
   Answer: Departmental Income Statement and MOR.

2. What does MOR stand for, and what is it?

   Answer: MOR stands for Monthly Operating Review. MOR is both a report and an event. The event is a meeting to discuss the report.

3. What is the difference between Exhibit 28 and Exhibit 31?

   Answer: Exhibit 31 includes estimated revenue deductions, benefit costs and other expenses incurred by the department that are not normally charged to them.

4. Which one is a truer reflection of the department manager's performance—Exhibit 28 or Exhibit 31?

   Answer: Although Exhibit 31 is a truer reflection of the entire department's performance, the only things missing from Exhibit 28 are things the department manager does not control, so the answer is that either could be used.

5. How does an MOR relate to the Departmental Income statement?

   Answer: The MOR is sometimes referred to as a "bridge" between the Departmental Income statement to your "story." The finance section de-codes the numbers back into operating metrics.

CHAPTER 18 SELF REVIEW QUESTIONS

---

1. Name the Seven Questions.
   Answer:

   • Are the financials correct?

- What are the unfavorable variances?

- Why did they occur?

- Have the events that caused them been corrected?

- If not, why not, and when will they be corrected?

- What help do you need to correct them?

- How are you doing this month?

2. What are the three steps to use to prepare for an MOR?
   Answer:

   - Block time.

   - Gather data.

   - Perform the review.

3. What are the two questions to ask yourself in determining if the financial statements are correct?
   Answer:

   - Are the expenses showing correct?

   - Are there any expenses missing?

4. On Exhibit 34 for Radiology, row 19 Column C shows a volume Adjusted budget of 61.55 Worked FTEs. Why is this number higher than the budgeted FTE number shown in column B?
   Answer: Column C increases the resources needed to cover the volume that was greater than budget.

5. Using Exhibit 34 for Radiology, how did the department achieve a better than budget Paid MH/Stat?

   Answer: Looking at Rows 12, 13 and 14, you see that although the department productivity was OVER budget on worked MH/Stat, Non-Productive times came in substantially under budget—enough to more than compensate for the unfavorable Worked hours per Stat variance.

About the Author

Denise Chamberlain is a hospital Chief Financial Officer (CFO) with 25 years of experience as both a healthcare finance executive and a professional teacher and educator. Her experience includes all levels of financial management for hospitals ranging from 25-bed Specialty hospitals to 1,000-bed tertiary teaching hospitals, including for-profit, not-for-profit and public systems.

As an honor graduate of Purdue University, a Certified Public Accountant, and a former Manager with Arthur Andersen & Co. in their worldwide headquarters for healthcare (Dallas, TX), Denise assisted in development of training classes and trained staff, both around the U.S. and Europe.

As a hospital CFO and finance executive, Denise has always understood that finance is a foreign language for most non-finance staff, and she has developed training classes to assist with daily and monthly financial management tasks, as well as with preparing capital and operating budgets.

She is Founder and CEO of Money to Care, LLC, a company dedicated to, and specializing in, hospital finance education and training. The company's web site is www.moneytocare.com.

Denise lives in Scottsdale, Arizona.